• HALSGROVE DISCOVER SERIES ➤

DARTMOOR
SUN

Jack Walker

HALSGROVE

First published in Great Britain in 2005

British Library Cataloguing-in-Publication Data
A CIP record for this title is available from the British Library

ISBN 1 84114 423 1

HALSGROVE
Halsgrove House
Lower Moor Way
Tiverton, Devon EX16 6SS
Tel: 01884 243242
Fax: 01884 243325
email: sales@halsgrove.com
website: www.halsgrove.com

Printed and bound by D'Auria Industrie Grafiche Spa, Italy

Contents

Acknowledgements

I wish to thank Yvonne Cook of the Open University's Open Eye Supplement to the *Independent* newspaper of 5 October 1999 for her article reporting my initial findings at the Hingston Hill monument. Grateful thanks are also extended to Elisabeth Stanbrook, Editor of *Dartmoor Magazine* numbers 63, 67,69 and 71.

Others who made valuable contributions include Tavistock artist John Estall for his sketch of Stonehenge. My photographs of the Bronze Age axes are courtesy of Martin Eddy, Moorland & Countryside Officer for Caradon Countryside Service. Thanks also to the staff of the Heatree Activity Centre, and Carolyn and Nigel of Lower Merripit for their work reconstructing prehistoric roundhouses.

I also extend thanks to members of Tavistock Astronomical Society, Tavistock Writers Group, Tavistock & District Local History Society, likewise to Shirley and Len who, together with my wife Jenny, positioned themselves as monthly sunset markers for photographs at Hingston Hill.

MOOR CARE

Please take care to protect Dartmoor's archaeological landscape.
Many sites are protected under the Ancient Monuments
and Archaeological Areas Act and you may be breaking
the law if you disturb them.

FOREWORD

There are two ways of looking at any landscape with regard to interpreting the signs that prehistoric man has left upon it. A scientist would ask us to look at the historic evidence, at the remains left by these early inhabitants, and to draw conclusions based upon what we can see. The social historian, on the other hand, might suggest we interpret these things through what we know of mankind's behaviour and habits, for despite the passing millennia are we not the same creature as our forebears?

The truth is that we will only ever partly deduce how our predecessors lived thousands of years ago, and how they thought. Though science provides us with ever more detailed evidence, there will always be a need for interpretation - even inspired guesses. One thing that history *has* taught us, especially that involving the interpretation of the Dartmoor landscape, is that whatever was once held to be fact can now be seen as mistaken.

However, this is not to decry the work of early antiquarians, for only by degrees does our knowledge advance, and we have them to thank for describing much that is now lost or destroyed. Countless archaeological features have disappeared from Dartmoor, prey to the ravages of time and at the hands of miners, farmers and others to whom a stone row would have meant an annoying obstruction or a convenient source of stone ideal for the completion of an urgent project.

Writing about prehistoric stone rows in the 1840s, Samuel Rowe makes particular reference to 'Those curious relics of the aboriginal period of our history,' which he and his colleagues firmly establish as an 'avenue, constructed for the performance of some solemn Arkite ceremonial.' Half a century later Robert Burnard dismisses the druidical connection so fondly adopted by earlier historians, and by the time R. Hansford Worth presents the first 'modern' survey of stone rows, again fifty years on, speculation has given way almost entirely to triangulation.

In 1991 I had the privilege of publishing the first of five volumes of Jeremy Butler's revolutionary work the *Dartmoor Atlas of Antiquities*. His was a superb contemporary interpretation of the archaeology of Dartmoor, the final volume of which established solid ground from which future interpretative battles could be fought with confidence. Yet this innovative expert acknowledges that science and archaeological studies have moved things forward even since his final volume was published in 1997.

And so on to *Dartmoor Sun*. On reading the first draft of Jack Walker's book I was struck by how refreshing and simple was his approach to a 'mystery' that, as we have seen, has been the cause of much speculation for centuries. Essentially here was an engineer's response to an engineering problem. Certainly if Jack had not been out on Dartmoor 'one evening, by accident' this book would never have been written. But many others have spent years examining the stone rows of Dartmoor, measuring and documenting every boulder, and yet they have missed what Jack saw in an instant. And, as with the solution to many mysteries, it is often better to look for the obvious.

Not that Jack, or I, would claim his work to be entirely novel, or even the last word on interpreting Dartmoor's stone rows. The

linking of ancient monuments to astronomical events is not new: Jack himself draws on evidence from Stonehenge and from those many archaeologists who have extended our knowledge in this field over recent decades. Others will undoubtedly arrive on the scene with fresh evidence and new theories.

The value of Jack's work lies principally in his specific interpretation of three of the seventy-plus stones rows on Dartmoor. Certainly he provides a clear and plausible explanation of the purpose of these artefacts; but it is after all a theory. For me the delight in reading this book, and which perhaps also strengthens my conviction that his theory is proved, lies in the straightforward way in which his revelation came about - 'one evening, by accident', and in the logical way he then proceeds to prove his case: the wooden poles and human markers Jack employs to help him would have been the same methods available to the builders of those rows over 4000 years ago.

Human ingenuity is universal and without bounds.

And for all of us who like to see a problem solved, or new light thrown on an old mystery, *Dartmoor Sun* is a fascinating read.

Simon Butler FRSA
The Publisher

Nothing's Lost

I hear their cry
In the cold wind's sigh.
I hear their laughter
In the sunshine that comes after.
And when I see the sun's warm face keep time
With stone monument's ancient rhyme,
I know nothing's lost;
It's all here in the peat
Feel it pushing at your feet.

Introduction

One evening, almost by accident, I was in the right place, at the right time to observe one of Dartmoor's ancient monuments as its builders' intended. This is the story of that night, the investigation that followed, and life under the Dartmoor sun thousands of years ago.

Dartmoor is like an unopened book that holds the secrets of the past five thousand years. It is a refuge from city strife, an ancient wilderness, a playground, a National Park; it is a record of thousands of voices singing and sighing through the ages. It is all this and more.

Perched on top of 368 square miles of granite, much of it above 1000 feet, the wilderness of the Dartmoor National Park crowns South West Britain. Peat bog reservoirs trapped over the granite, shake underfoot as they slowly release rainwater to feed the streams that will become Dartmoor's rivers.

Twenty thousand years ago Dartmoor was in the grip of the last Ice Age. Parts of the North Sea and the English Channel were dry land, and Britain was part of mainland Europe.

Twelve thousand years ago the world entered an interglacial period in which sea levels gradually increased as the ice melted. Hunter-gatherers followed herds of animals over a Britain that was connected by land-bridges to Europe.

About eight thousand years ago, sea levels had risen sufficiently to form the North Sea, the English Channel and the Irish Sea, giving birth to the British Isles.

Dartmoor was occupied from Neolithic times (4200BC to 2000BC) through the Bronze Age (2000BC to 700BC) until it became depopulated in the Iron Age. From then on it remained largely unoccupied until medieval tinners came to gather its minerals.

A rich diversity of important archaeological sites exists on Dartmoor, conserved both by their remoteness from the beaten track and the respect of those who followed. For a while this regard for the past temporarily ceased with the arrival of a few Victorian treasure-seekers and grave plunderers, but at last the moor was saved from their ravages, eventually becoming Dartmoor National Park in 1951.

Dartmoor contains unique evidence of settlements, daily life, monuments and the ceremonial sites of those who occupied it from the Neolithic through the Bronze Age and beyond. Despite the ravages of 'civilisation' much of Dartmoor's past remains intact and forms a unique link to our ancestors. The moor is blessed with a wealth of hut circles, stone rows, stone circles and ancient ceremonial complexes left in trust to all who follow.

There are several worthy, scientifically surveyed and detailed accounts of the layout of Dartmoor's antiquities but disappointingly few radiocarbon dates. Although it is important to have the measure of these antiquities, it is more interesting to know what they were for, how were they used and what they tell of the lives and beliefs of their builders. *Dartmoor Sun* is an attempt to answer some of these questions based on the well-preserved remains of three of Dartmoor's ancient ceremonial complexes. Photographic evidence is used to record what to the builders may have been significant events.

The technology used at these three ancient Dartmoor complexes is as relevant now as it was when they were constructed. It may be easily understood and observed operating as reliably today as it did 4000 years ago. With the advantages of modern technology, information from books, computerised maps and airborne photography it would be interesting to apply the findings and techniques described here to more of Dartmoor's ancient monuments.

In order to corroborate the results described and photographed in *Dartmoor Sun* they are compared first to those obtained at Stonehenge and then to more distant ancient monuments. From these comparisons conclusions are drawn which may shed a little more light on the lives of some of our ancient ancestors.

It is interesting to speculate who may be examining our technology 4000 years from now and what they will think of our lives, but that's another story.

Thousand of years ago the people of Dartmoor left records of their lives and culture in the landscape. Some of this ancient chronicle has survived and continues to faithfully tell its story. *Dartmoor Sun* attempts to put it into words.

Chapter One

To the High Moor

Trees at Norsworthy Bridge.

Note: Ordnance Survey, Outdoor Leisure Map 28 – Dartmoor, 1:25,000 scale *shows all three of the Dartmoor monuments examined in* Dartmoor Sun.

Hingston Hill's Ancient Stone Circle and Stone Row are at Grid Reference SX587693

The ancient monument on Hingston Hill was the first I witnessed as the builders' intended. It was sunset on the day of the summer solstice; but in order to fully appreciate the setting, it is essential to know the way up to the monument, which is in itself a journey through time.

From Norsworthy Bridge to Cuckoo Rock and Hingston Tor

Dartmoor's Burrator Reservoir is a beauty spot some ten miles north of the city of Plymouth and was opened in 1898. Around its perimeter are several popular picnic areas.

Starting from the Norsworthy Bridge (OS SX568693) car park, which lies at the eastern end of Burrator Reservoir, the track follows the northern edge of Middleworth Plantation. Three hundred and fifty metres along the track, on the right, stands the two-storey granite shell of an abandoned Middleworth Farm building. One kilometre beyond this to the left of the track lie the exposed foundations of Deancombe Farm.

There were three farms in the area, Norsworthy, Middleworth and Deancombe, with records dating back to the thirteenth century.[1]

From Deancombe the track passes through a gateway to become narrower and more difficult. Not far ahead a smaller path winds its way left, up to the distinctive shape of Cuckoo Rock. Above Cuckoo Rock and 600 metres ahead to the north is Hingston Tor (SX 586692), with Combshead Tor 300 metres away to the east.

The Middleworth Plantation track.

Middleworth.

Deancombe Farm.

Left: *Approaching Cuckoo Rock.*
Below: *Cuckoo Rock.*

Hingston Hill's stone circle and row.

From the top of Hingston Tor a magnificent 12 metre diameter stone circle and 350 metres long stone row lie 150 metres to the north-east.

Note: For some unknown reason the monuments on Hingston Hill are commonly referred to as being on Down Tor, which is quite wrong. Down Tor is the distinctive tor 700 metres west of Hingston Tor. On the Ordnance Survey, Outdoor Leisure 28, Dartmoor map, Hingston Tor is not identified, but the height of the tor is marked on the map as '372' metres and the stone row is shown clearly. Hingston Hill is the broad whale-backed ridge on which the row and circle lie. Hingston Tor (SX586692) is the rock at the highest point of Hingston Hill.

Below left and right: *The row from the circle.*

Chapter Two

Summer Solstice at Hingston Hill

Summer Solstice Sunset

One perfect evening during a walk on Dartmoor with my wife we rested by the ancient stone circle and row at Hingston Hill to watch the summer solstice sunset. As the sun neared the horizon it aligned with a large cairn and the stone circle.

I returned to Hingston Hill at 5:00am a few days later to see if there were any alignments with the rising sun. What I saw then may not have been witnessed for several thousand years and led me on a quest for an explanation.

Summer solstice sunset at Hingston Hill.

Looking west from the blocking stone.

Pictorial view of the Hingston Hill site.

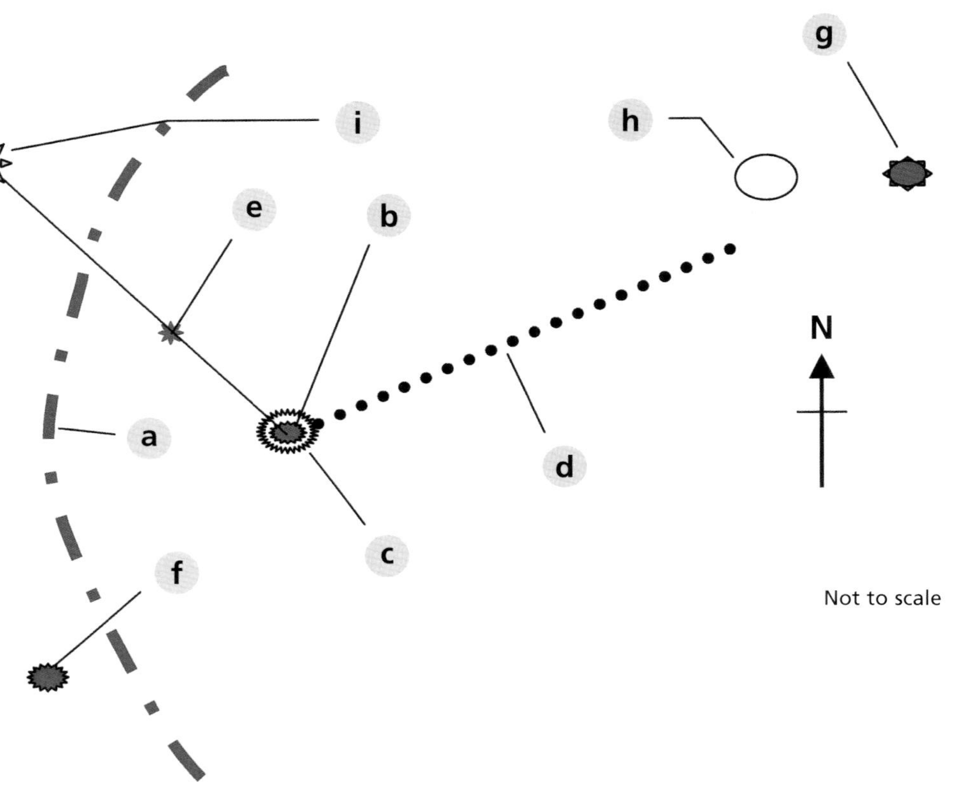

Key:

- **a** Ancient raised boundary work
- **b** Cairn inside stone circle
- **c** Stone circle – 12 m diameter
- **d** Stone row – 350 m long
- **e** Cairn aligned with midsummer sunset from circle
- **f** Small tor at site high point
- **g** Large cairn in line with stone row
- **h** Stone enclosure
- **i** Setting sun

Looking west from the large cairn in line with the row.

Summer Solstice Sunrise

In the pre-dawn glow at 4:15am I left my car at the Norsworthy Bridge car park.

The sky was clear as I headed up the track past Middleworth Plantation with my footsteps sounding hollow on the dry surface. I was thinking how the road alongside the reservoir was full of rabbits, which are seldom seen in daylight, when I heard a drumming noise that got rapidly louder.

Norsworthy Bridge car park.

It was too dark to see far up the track but I moved out of the way in time to see a grey stallion lead a herd of ponies at a trot in single file down the lane. He looked at me accusingly without slowing as he passed by about three metres away, as if to say 'You shouldn't be here.'

Higher up, alongside the path near the remains of Deancombe Farm, the sky began to lighten as I watched a line of sheep, led by a ram, pick their way daintily through ferns along an all but invisible track. Again the leading animal looked at me reproachfully; he appeared to know exactly where he was leading his flock and seemed slightly aggrieved that I should be here.

On the moor to my left I approached Cuckoo Rock, wondering what the ancient Dartmoor inhabitants thought of its strangely sculpted bulk. Then skirting around Combshead Tor I headed across swampy ground towards Hingston Tor, catching occasional glimpses of the stone row.

Cattle lay on the slopes of Combeshead Tor, more alert and organised than during daylight, with the larger animals standing guard at the edges of the herd.

As I approached the monument the sky was clear in all directions except for one. There was a mist between the monument and the sun as it rose over the horizon in the north-east, lighting the haze from within.

As I walked past the eastern end of the 350-metre stone row the sun broke through the mist. It cast my gigantic shadow far over the land with my head and shoulders projected clearly across the most easterly standing stone (the blocking stone), which had its main face at right angles to the sun.

Each standing stone cast its long shadow about one degree south of the next standing stone. I realised that the monument's stones were in the process of becoming connected by their shadows, which were slowly coming into alignment with each other as the sun moved across the sky. Soon they would form a continuous shadow line (350 metres long) through the sunlit standing stones.

Surprised at this unexpected event I hurried along the stone row towards the circle. When I approached the three megaliths closest to the circle, I saw that their shadows had formed a triple alignment.

Shadow on the blocking stone.
Explanation: It is not unusual on Dartmoor to find that the last stone in a row is set across the row, as if to block it. Such a stone is therefore often called a blocking stone. Standing at the eastern end of the row my shadow was cast on to the blocking stone; black shadow on white stone.

Summer solstice sunrise. Mist at Hingston Hill stone circle.

The triple alignment.

Explanation: The pointed shadow from the third megalith cast its shadow on the face of the second megalith. The second cast its shadow on the face of the first and the first cast its shadow into the stone circle. This effect lasted for a short time until the ground mist obscured the sun again. I walked past the stone circle and turned to take a photograph looking across the circle, into the mist, towards the sun. At 08:00am I was back home in bed. It was Sunday morning.

Over the next few weeks I tried to understand what I had witnessed and realised I needed more photographs in order to analyse the total effect of the summer solstice sunrise on the monument. These photographs were more difficult to obtain than expected as it was necessary to have perfect weather at the site at sunrise and there was usually either cloud or mist obscuring the sun. A year later the conditions were ideal with the following results:

Photographs and Diagrams of Summer Solstice Sunrise at Hingston Hill

Notes:

1 *The word 'solstice' means, 'sun and still' referring to the fact that around the time of the solstices the sun appears to follow the same path through the sky for a week or two each side of the actual day of the solstice. For this reason the effects of the sun on the monument are substantially the same over this period.*

2 *The word 'megalith' simply means 'big stone'.*

Sunrise.

Explanation: First light of summer solstice sunrise catches the tip of the main megalith at the Hingston Hill stone circle.

The row's shadows align.
Explanation: As the summer solstice sun comes into alignment with the row, each of the shadows of the smaller stones' shadows appear to be spaced so that they just touch the next stone.

The three megaliths.
Explanation: The shadows of the three main megaliths align.

The first megalith – the gnomon.
Explanation: At the summer solstice alignment the symmetrically-pointed shadow of the second megalith is displayed centrally on the eastern side of the main megalith, and the distinct shape of the first megalith (the gnomon) is cast into the centre of the stone circle.

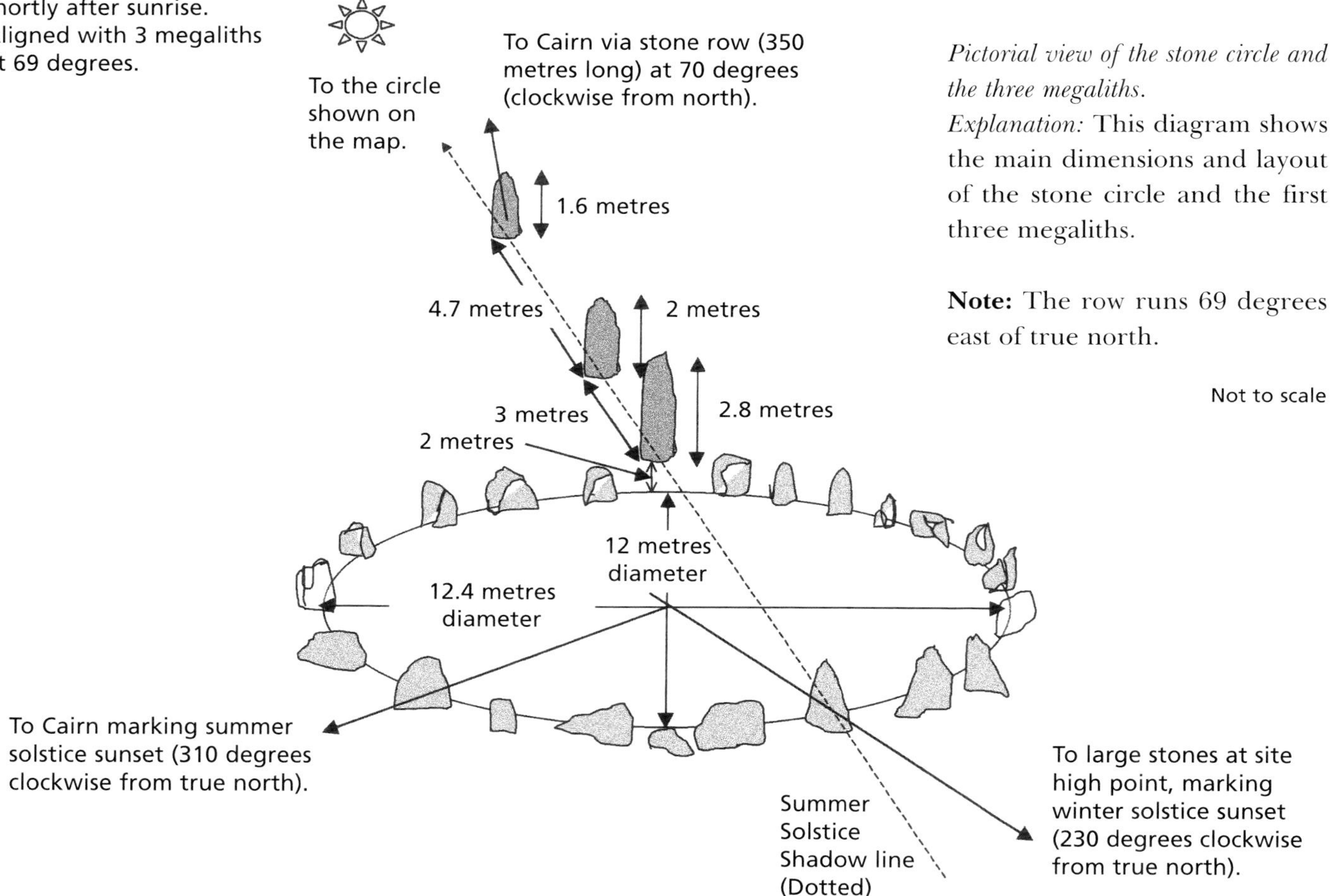

Pictorial view of the stone circle and the three megaliths.

Explanation: This diagram shows the main dimensions and layout of the stone circle and the first three megaliths.

Note: The row runs 69 degrees east of true north.

Not to scale

This is the rough arc marked on the map as 'Boundary Work', which is approximately at a radius of 100 metres from the centre of the stone circle. It is approximately 300 metres long and extends past each of the solstice markers. The entire area is covered in ancient mounds.

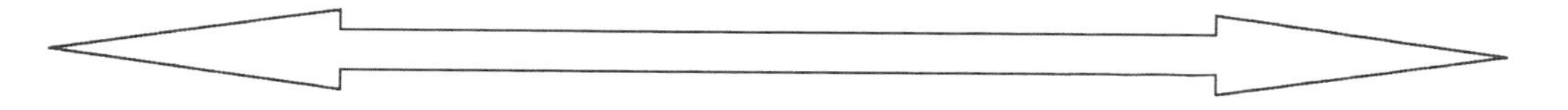

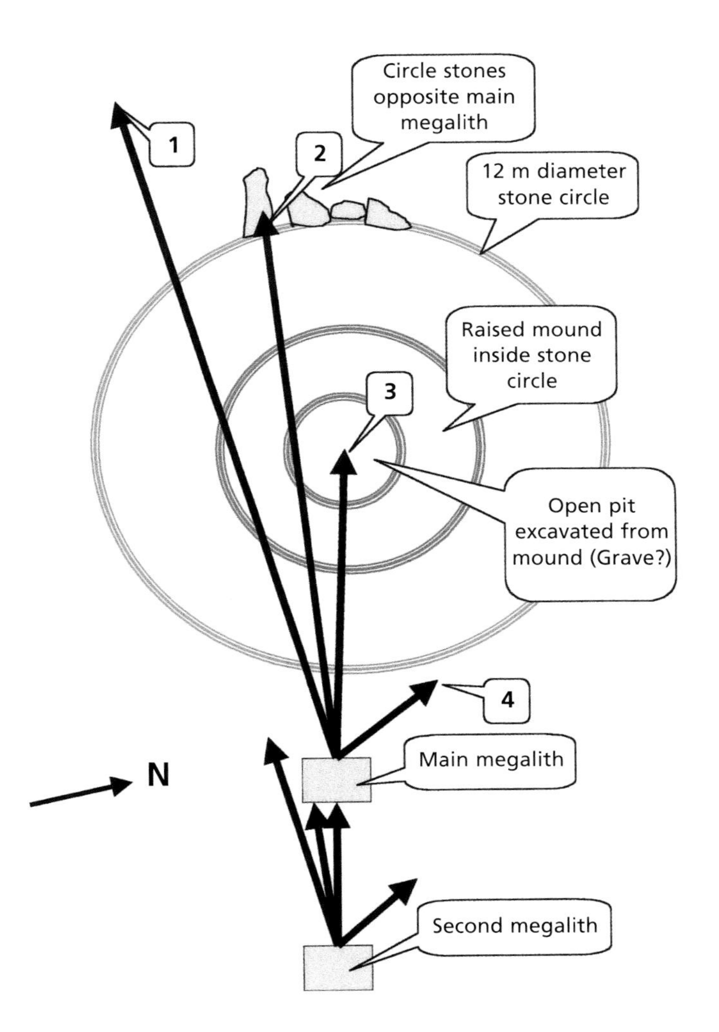

The moving shadow of the gnomon at summer solstice.

Explanation: This diagram shows how the shadow thrown by the main megalith (the gnomon) moves across the stone circle from 05:45am to 10:00am at the summer solstice.

The second megalith's shadow moves across the east face of the main megalith from about 06:00am indicating the time and position of the gnomon's shadow inside the stone circle. It is central at about 06:45am.

Although the diagram is not strictly to scale, the main megalith is about 2.7 metres high and set back from the 12-meter diameter stone circle by about 2 metres.

Key: Main megalith (the gnomon)

1 Its shadow at about 05.45am.

2 Its shadow at about 06.10am.

3 Its shadow at 06.45am.

4 Its shadow at 10.00am.

Note: At midday the gnomon's shadow is at its shortest and pointing north. After midday the path of the gnomon's shadow traces a mirror image of the morning shadow.

Gnomon shadow 1 (looking west).
Explanation: The main megalith's shadow is outside the circle until about 06:10am (see Key 1 of diagram – p.27). Then the rising sun shortens it and moves it clockwise until it is projected on to the inner face of the circle stone opposite (see Key 2 of diagram – p.27, and photograph: Gnomon shadow 2 – below).

Gnomon shadow 2.
Explanation: At about 06:10am the gnomon's shadow is projected on the inner face of the pointed stone on the west side of the circle.

Above and right: *Gnomon shadow 3.*
Explanation: At about 06:45am the tip of the gnomon's shadow is over the cist (stone-box grave) at the centre of the stone circle. Also at this time the slim symmetrically-pointed shadow of the second megalith is displayed centrally on the eastern face of the main megalith.

Left: *Gnomon shadow 3a.*
Explanation: Looking back (east) across the stone circle a few minutes after 06:45am, with a hand shielding the sun's glare from the camera lens. The shadow of the gnomon has moved past the cist (grave) in the centre of the circle.

Below: *Gnomon shadow 3b.*
Explanation: Looking west. The gnomon's shadow a few minutes after 06:45am, has moved through the centre of the circle.

Gnomon shadow 4.

Explanation: By 10:00am the main megalith's (the gnomon's) shadow is outside the circle (see Key 4 of diagram – p.27).

Circle and shadow from south.
Explanation: Looking from the south of the monument a few minutes after the triple alignment.

Looking west – the raised horizon.
Explanation: This photograph shows three important features of the site:

(i) The summer solstice sunset marker cairn.

(ii) The highest point of the western horizon from the circle, which marks the winter solstice sunset direction.

(iii) The raised horizon between (i) and (ii) that provides the ideal situation for marking and recording sunset positions throughout the year and hence creating a calendar. This feature is enhanced by the ancient raised wall that follows the shape of the circle between (i) and (ii) and is marked on Ordnance Survey 1:25,000 Outdoor Leisure Map 28.

Left: *Summer solstice sunrise alignment from the eastern cairn.*
Explanation: Aligned with the row and 225 metres beyond the blocking stone is a large cairn. Taken from here at summer solstice sunrise, the photograph shows the monument in the distance. Sheeps Tor is on the skyline about 2.25km behind Hingston Tor.

Below: *Early morning at the circle.*
Explanation: Hikers take a well-earned 10:00am rest at the circle at summer solstice.

Hingston Hill Sunrises from April to August

The shadows of the standing stones first come into sunrise alignment from about the 21 April and continue to do so at some time each morning until the 21 August, which is for four 30-day periods (moonths or months). It is thought that the apparent period of the moons cycle, which to the nearest day is 30 days, was used to divide the year into 12 month's (see Chapter 3). However at times other than the summer solstice the sun is lower in the sky when the alignment occurs. This causes the shadow of the main megalith to lengthen westwards (in proportion to the number of days from the solstice), taking the tip of the gnomon's shadow out beyond the centre of the circle.

This annual graphic situation caused by the layout of the monument, with its shadows shortening, lengthening and aligning, may have been used in ancient times to predict and determine the time of the summer solstice. The fact that the tip of the shadow of the gnomon bisects the circle and touches the centre of the mound (grave?) at summer solstice suggests the monument had both practical and ceremonial importance for its creators.

The discovery that the monument continues faithfully to repeat its annual message several millennia after its construction (it is thought to be from three to five thousand years old) is a tribute to the ingenuity of those who designed and built it.

Perhaps these findings take us a little closer to understanding the builders of this sublimely beautiful ancient monument.

There are too many coincidences here at the time of the summer solstice for the alignments to be considered as pure chance. They suggest that one of the functions of the monument was to visually show the approach, arrival and departure of the summer solstice which would have been a time of fundamental significance to the monument's constructors so many years ago.

Gnomon shadows.

Some of the (deliberate) coincidences that the monument uses may be observed in the photograph (right). They include:

(i) The shape of the gnomon, which is traditionally the form favoured to cast a pointed shadow across a marker, as used in a sundial for example.

(ii) The pointed symmetry of the shadow of the second megalith (like the hand of a clock), which is ideal for indicating the timing of the solstice. This shadow is displayed on the east face of the gnomon, whose width corresponds with the approach, arrival and passing of the gnomon's solstice shadow through the circle over the critical time from 06:00 to 07:15am.

(iii) The face of the gnomon is ideally placed to display and contrast with the symmetrical and centrally-pointed shadow of the second megalith.

(iv) The carefully placed position of the gnomon in relation to the burial mound, so that at the summer solstice the tip of the shadow traces a path across the middle of the grave in the stone circle.

Another striking feature of this site is the raised horizon to the west of the stone circle. This raised western horizon (it is higher than the stone circle) is continuous from the mound that marks the summer solstice sunset position through the small tor that marks the winter solstice sunset position.

An illuminating feature of this monument is the timing of its midsummer morning alignment. It overcomes the problem caused by the fact that mist or low clouds at first light often obscure the

Full pictorial view of Hingston Hill monument. *Explanation:* The raised horizon made the monument ideal for recording the positions of the setting sun throughout the year and thereby of knowing the time of year (the date).

position of the sun on the horizon. The Hingston Hill monument aligns early in the morning with the sun above the horizon thus giving more impact to ceremonial proceedings. This may have significant implications for our understanding of other ancient monuments: *It is not necessary for a monument based on the sun's position to point directly at the sun at sunrise or sunset.* Stonehenge is a good example. Contrary to common belief it never did strictly align with the rising midsummer sun on the horizon, it aligned a few minutes after sunrise, possibly for the same reason as the ancient monument on Dartmoor's Hingston Hill.

Key:

a Ancient raised boundary work
b Cairn inside stone circle
c Stone circle – 12m diameter
d Stone row – 350m long
e Cairn aligned with midsummer sunset from circle
f Small tor at site high point
g Large cairn in line with stone row
h Stone enclosure
i Setting summer solstice sun direction
j Setting winter solstice sun direction
k Setting winter solstice shadow

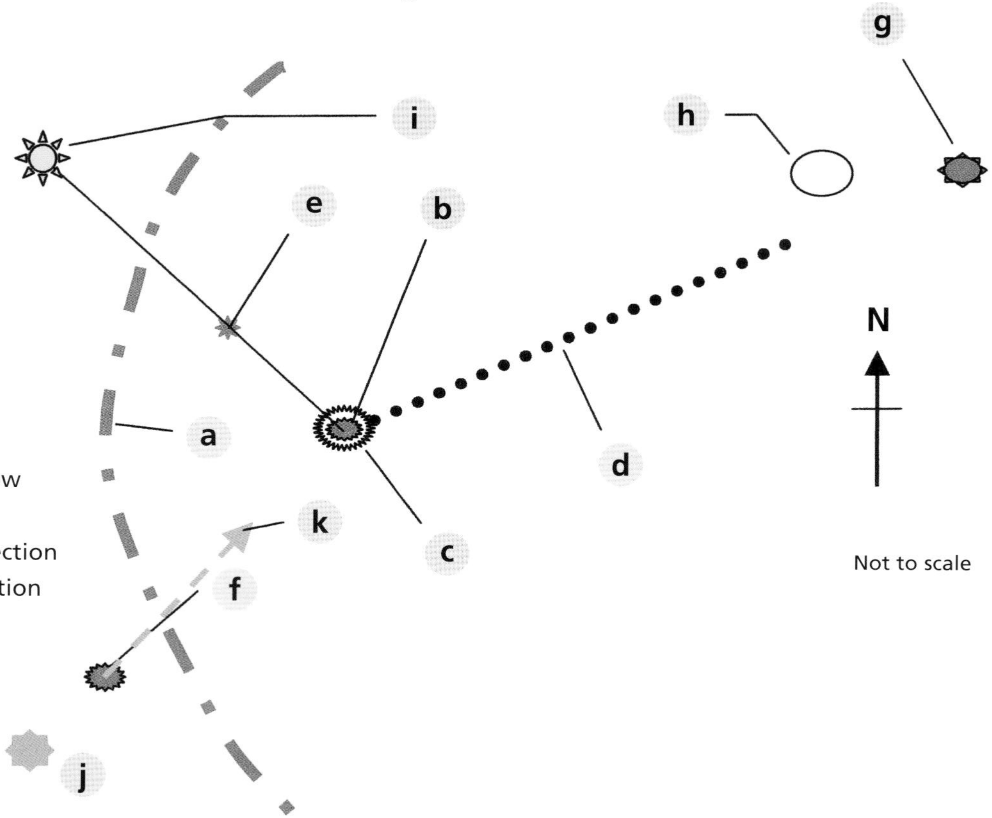

N

Not to scale

Location, Location, Location.
The Hingston Hill Site

When viewed from the small tor that stands on the highest point of Hingston Hill, this is an imposing site, worthy of its ancient monuments.

Right: *Hingston Hill's small tor.*
Explanation: The Hingston Hill high point tor becomes very important to the ancient monument at the winter solstice, when the sun sets behind Sheeps Tor which is on the horizon behind Hingston Tor.

The photograph right, and on the following two pages show the aspect clockwise from the top of Hingston Tor.

South of Hingston Hill
Explanation: In the south, the granite cubes of Combshead Tor dominate the horizon, beyond these and 2.5km further south are the stone rows and Giant's Basin of Drizzle Combe (Drizzlecombe).

West of Hingston Hill.
Explanation: To the west is Burrator Reservoir and the three tors in a line are respectively, Down Tor, Leather Tor and Sharpitor.

North-west of Hingston hill.
Explanation: On the right of the photograph just beyond the far trees and on the horizon are a line of tors including, Cox Tor, the Staple Tors and Great Mis Tor. In the valley at the foot of these tors lies the ancient ceremonial complex at Merrivale.

Above and above right: *North-east and east of Hingston Hill.*
Explanation: The stone circle is to the north-east, and the row points 69 degrees east from true north.

Right: *South-east.*
Explanation: Looking south-east over the circle towards Eylesbarrow.

Chapter Three

Dartmoor Sun

Sunrise

At Dartmoor's latitude on a level site, the position of the sunrise at the horizon varies from 50 degrees east of north at the summer solstice to 130 degrees east of north at the winter solstice. This is a total change of the position of sunrises throughout the year of 80 degrees and repeats every year. To know the position of the sun at sunrise throughout the year is to know the time of the year (the date), which is also true for the annual sunsets.

Sunset

At Dartmoor's latitude on a level site the position of the sunset at the horizon varies from 50 degrees west of north at the summer solstice to 130 degrees west of north at the winter solstice. This is a total change of the position of sunsets throughout the year of 80 degrees and repeats every year. To know the positions of the sun at sunset throughout the year is to know the time of the year (the date).

Explanation (p.41):
Summer Solstice:
At the summer solstice (21 June) the sun is in its most northerly position and rises at position '1R' which is 50 degrees east of north. The sun then continues to gain height travelling towards the south until at midday it is due south and at its highest daily and annual position.

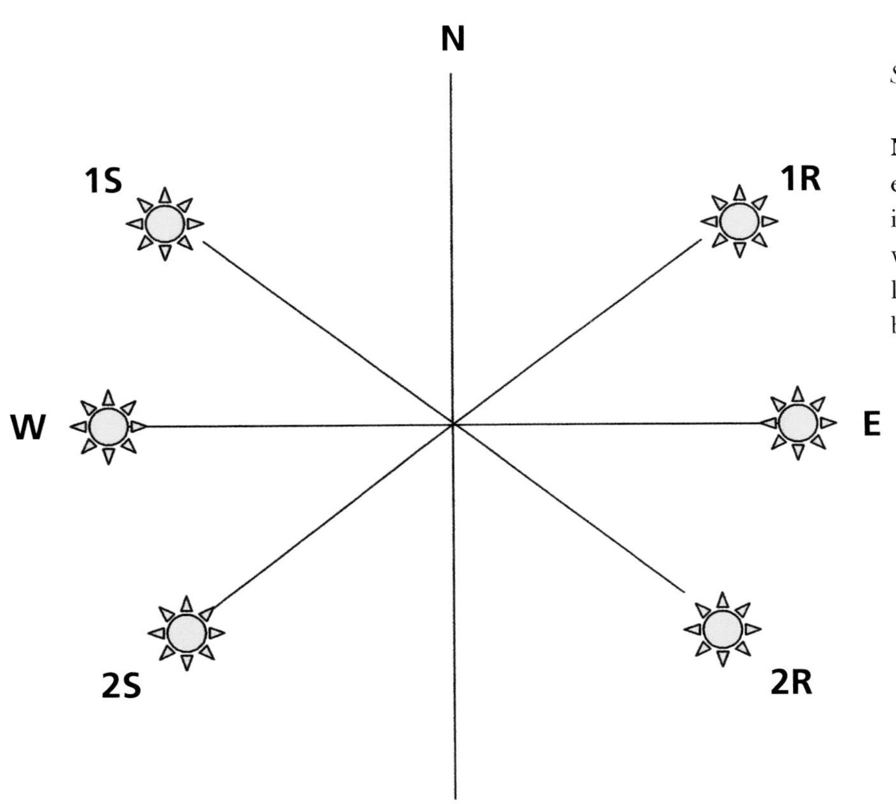

Sunrise and Sunset Positions on Dartmoor.

Note: The diagram is for a level site. For example if the sun rises behind a hill that is higher than the observing position it will rise a little later than it would on a level site and its rise position will differ by a corresponding amount.

Key:

N, S, E & W	Cardinal points of the compass.
1R	The sunrise position at the summer solstice.
1S	The sunset position at the summer solstice.
E	The sunrise position at the autumn and spring equinox.
W	The sunset position at the autumn and spring equinox.
2R	The sunrise position at the winter solstice.
2S	The sunset position at the winter solstice.

After midday the sun loses height travelling towards the north-west until it sets at position '1S' which is 50 degrees west of north. Daylight lasts for 16 hours.

Each day after the summer solstice the sun rises a little further south until the autumn equinox.

Autumn Equinox:
At the autumn equinox (23 September) the sun rises due east (90 degrees east of north) at position 'E'. The sun continues to gain height travelling towards the south until at midday it is due south.

After midday the sun loses height travelling towards the west until it sets at position 'W' which is 90 degrees west of north. Daylight lasts for 12 hours. Each day after this the sun rises a little further south until the winter solstice.

Winter Solstice:
At the winter solstice (21 December) the sun is in its most southerly position and rises at position '2R' which is 130 degrees east of north (180–50). The sun then continues to gain height travelling towards the south until at midday it is due south and at its lowest southerly (due south) daily and annual position.

After midday the sun loses height travelling towards the south-west until it sets at position '2S' which is 130 degrees west of north (180–50). Daylight lasts for 8 hours. Each day after this the sun rises a little further north until the spring equinox.

Spring Equinox:
At the spring equinox (21 March) the sun rises due east (90 degrees east of north) at position 'E'. The sun continues to gain height travelling towards the south until at midday it is due south.

After midday the sun loses height travelling towards the west until it sets at position 'W' which is 90 degrees west of north. Daylight lasts for 12 hours.

Each day after this the sun rises a little further north until the next summer solstice when the sequence repeats itself annually as it did 4000 years ago and for untold millennia before that. Knowledge of sun positions during the year was widely used throughout the world in ancient times as the basis of many calendars.

The Reason for the Seasons

It is the tilt of Earth's spin axis (currently about 23.5 degrees) as the planet makes its annual round of the sun that causes the seasons. This tilt takes the sun's path higher across the sky in summer and lower in winter.

The annual movement of the sun may have been used on Dartmoor and throughout much of the ancient world to regulate peoples' lives. Its discovery would have had a significant effect on the civilisation process. A 50-degree azimuth sunset/sunrise angle applies at Dartmoor's latitude. This sunrise/sunset angle increases to 90 degrees at the equator and reduces to zero at the poles, although the principal of using this phenomenon to tell the time of year appears to have been used in extensively in various forms in ancient world.

The 50 degree (sunrise/sunset) angle is calculated to have been closer to 49 degrees in 4000BC but fortunately this is not a sufficient change to have a significant effect on these observations of Dartmoor's ancient monuments. The amount of water vapour in the atmosphere may also cause a small variation in the apparent angle of the sun due to the refraction of its light.

For the technically minded:
The Earth behaves like a spinning top but its spin axis has a slight wobble called precession. Precession's wobble takes about 26 000 years to complete a cycle and consequently four thousand years ago the Earth's spin axis was in a slightly different position relative to the sun. This caused the sun (four thousand years ago) to rise about 0.93 degrees further north at the summer solstice and 0.93 degrees further south at the winter solstice. The positions of the equinoxes were not affected.

It is significant to note that the present solstice alignments on all three Dartmoor monuments show this predicted difference.

The Moon

Several distinguished authors have linked various ancient monuments' alignments to the rising and setting positions of the moon on the horizon, they may be correct to do so but such alignments are difficult to prove.

One problem is that it takes the moon 18.6 years to complete a full cycle and in this time the moon's rise and set positions occur at a bewildering number of places on the horizon. A friend suggested that it is as if the moon is playing 'lotto' with its watchers making them guess where it will pop up next. It is not impossible, but it is very difficult to achieve an accurate moon alignment prediction system for the entire 18.6-year cycle, and to achieve it an accurate annual calendar is necessary. The result is that at sites such as Merrivale a sun calendar was required before an 18.6-year moon positional prediction system could exist.

Note: *An interesting feature of the moon as observed from Earth is that it appears to take on average of 29.54 days to complete a cycle from one full moon to the next full moon. This is 30 days to the nearest day and is the reason why a 30-day period became known as a 'moonth' or month.*

Chapter Four

Winter Solstice at Hingston Hill

Hingston Hill Midwinter Sunset – 30 December 2001

It was 3.20 p.m. on 30 December 2001 and I had to move fast. Three times previously I had tried to photograph the winter solstice sunset here. On the first occasion I was too late, on the others clouds got in the way. Now, with perfect conditions, things were happening that I had not expected and there were only twelve shots in my new and unfamiliar digital camera.

With no time to waste I stood on the ancient, artificially raised horizon whose shadow was creeping down the slope towards the stone circle.

Having calculated that the small tor on the highest point of Hingston Hill would be in direct line with the winter solstice setting sun, the stone circle and the main menhir (megalith). I climbed on the top of the small tor, with my winter solstice sunset shadow moving clockwise with the sun and extending towards the ancient raised boundary work (wall) in the approximate direction of the circle. I estimated that in a few minutes' time, when the sun sat on the horizon, my long shadow would reach the ancient wall and align with the stone circle.

It was not possible to see the circle from the tor but the top half of the gnomon (main megalith) and the shadow it cast beyond the circle were visible. If the burial mound inside the circle was complete it is probable that its top would also be visible.

Was it the original intention that at midwinter sunset, people on the burial mound would watch the shadow of a person silhouetted against the setting sun on the narrow tor extend and point towards them?

Or perhaps the long shadow from the tor was used to calibrate the monument (and the date) with the winter solstice sunset.

Something that I had not anticipated happened at the stone circle as the sun set:

(i) The shadows of the three tall and pointed stones at the south-west of the circle passed slowly over the burial mound.

(ii) The shadow of the circle stone nearest the main menhir moved until it was perfectly framed on the western face of the menhir at sunset. This is very similar to the effect that I later found at winter solstice sunset at the Merrivale ancient ceremonial complex.

Just before sunset two young couples arrived at the circle. Although they obviously enjoyed the magnificence of the monument and its location at this auspicious sunset, I suspect they failed to recognise much that was happening. I hope they return, this time to witness the ancient monument faithfully fulfilling its annual tryst with the dying sun as the ancient builders' intended.

Photographs of Winter Solstice Sunset at Hingston Hill

The ancient raised boundary work.
Explanation: The walking pole stands on the ancient raised boundary work (stone wall) in line with where the winter solstice sun will set as viewed from the circle. This wall follows the shape of the circle at a radius of about 100 metres from the centre, and is where the sun will be seen to set throughout the year when viewed from the circle.

The main megalith viewed from the small tor.

The circle with shadows near sunset.
Explanation: A few minutes before winter solstice sunset the shadows of the three pointed stones on the circle nearest the sunset move clockwise towards the centre of the circle. Also the shadow of the circle stone to the south-west of the main megalith moves clockwise across the main megalith.

Megalith with shadow near sunset
Explanation: The pointed shadow of one of the south-west stones is cast on the face of the stone to the south-west of the main megalith as it in turn casts its shadow on the face of the main megalith.

Above: *The circle at sunset.*
Explanation: As the setting sun reaches the horizon its shadow creeps across the circle and the shadow of the stone to the south-west of the main megalith is clearly displayed in the centre of the west face of the main megalith as the winter solstice sun sets.

Right: *Megalith with shadow alignment at sunset.*
Explanation: Looking across the circle to the perfectly aligned shadow at winter solstice sunset.

Shadow of a figure on Hingston Hill Tor near sunset.
Explanation: A few minutes before winter solstice sunset the shadow cast by a figure on the tor is extending and moving clockwise towards the ancient wall and the circle.

Figure on Hingston Hill Tor at winter solstice sunset.
Explanation: At winter solstice sunset the shadow of a figure on the tor extends to the ancient wall in line with the circle.

Notes:

Technical Note: Due to the precession of the Earth's spin axis over the period from 2000BC to AD2000 the position of summer and winter solstice sunrise and solstice sunset positions have been slowly changing so that:

The summer solstice sun now rises and sets about 0.93 degrees further north than it did in 2000BC.

The winter solstice sun now rises and sets about 0.93 degrees further south than it did in 2000BC.

There is no change in the sunrise and sunset position at the equinoxes.

The actual change is 55 minutes of a degree or 55/60 = 0.917 degrees according to 'SkyMap Pro8' which is an astronomical computer program. And 56/60 = 0.933 degrees according to 'REDSHIFT 5' which is another astronomical computer program.

Allowing for the above 0.93 degree shift in sunset position from when the monument was constructed, the accuracy of the winter solstice sunset shadow is remarkable. The shadow moves about one degree every four minutes and is approximately 100m long at winter solstice sunset.

The shadow on the megalith at winter solstice sunset.

Explanation: The megalith perfectly frames the winter solstice sunset shadow at sunset. This was why I was here; it was what I had thought could happen, but the reality far exceeded any calculation. Four thousand years ago someone may have stood atop this tor as the winter solstice sun set behind them, with their shadow pointing to the gnomon, celebrating the turning of the sun and the start of a new year.

Chapter Five

DRIZZLECOMBE

Winter Solstice at Drizzlecombe Stone Rows

Three ancient stone rows straddle the Dartmoor valley of Drizzlecombe, at Ordnance Survey grid reference SX 592669. Each row runs approximately north-east from a large standing stone (terminal menhir) at its lower south-west end, up through a line of small standing stones to a cairn at the north-east.

We can't be certain of the purpose of these rows and the huge adjacent cairn known as the Giant's Basin. However, it is interesting to note that at least two of the rows and possibly the Giant's Basin itself have alignments with the sun at the winter solstice and may have been used to measure the approach and passing of this important time of the year.

Drizzlecombe's ancient monuments.
Explanation: This annotated photograph was taken on 8 February 2002 looking up Row 1 to the north-east and shows the layout of the site.

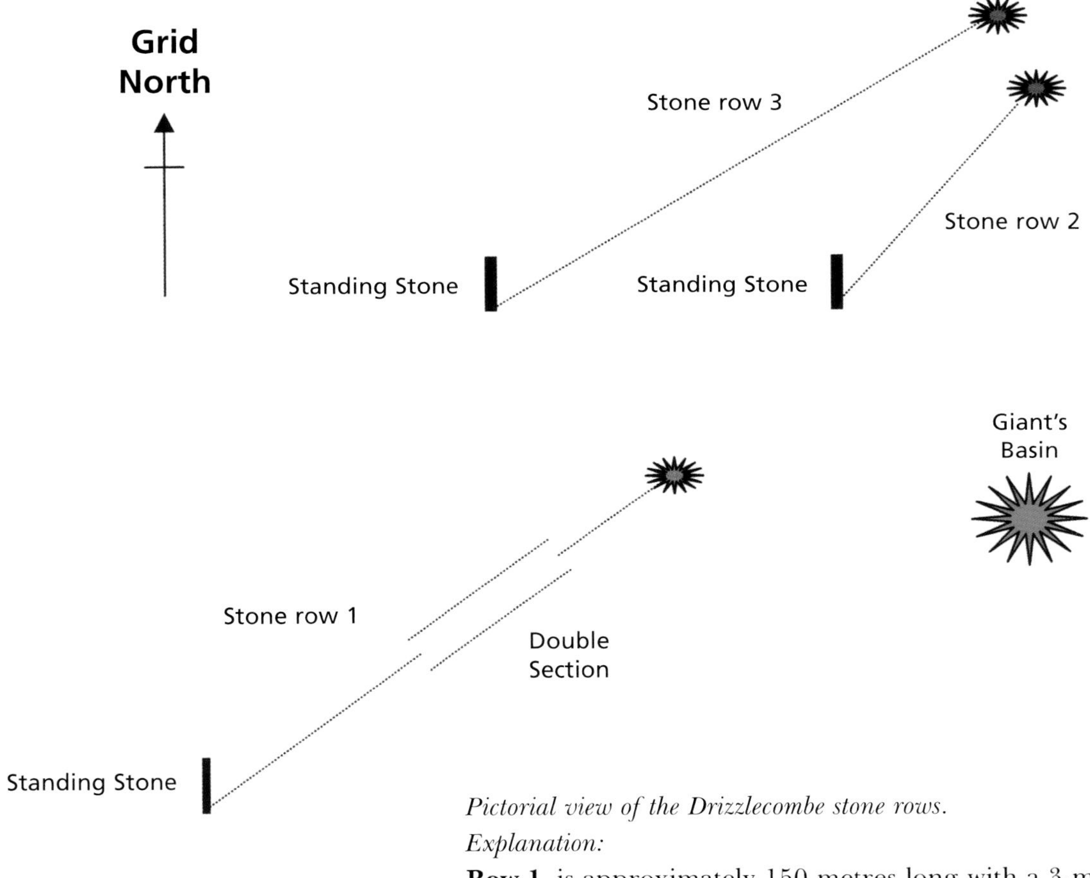

Pictorial view of the Drizzlecombe stone rows.

Explanation:

Row 1 is approximately 150 metres long with a 3-metre tall terminal menhir and is oriented 48 degrees east of grid north.

Row 2 is approximately 83 metres long with a 4.2 metre high terminal menhir (the tallest on Dartmoor) and is oriented 42 degrees east of grid north.

Row 3 is approximately 150 metres long with a 2.3 metre tall terminal menhir and is oriented 52 degrees east of grid north.

The Giant's Basin lies 80 metres south-east of Row 3's terminal menhir.

Row 2 has the tallest standing stone on Dartmoor at 4.2 metres high.

Looking south-west down Row 1 to its menhir.

The sequence of alignments was approximately:

Row 2 alignment at 3.00pm.
Row 1 alignment at 3.40pm.
Row 3 alignment at 3.50pm.

Each day throughout the year, the shadows thrown by each of the three terminal menhirs rotate clockwise across their stone rows like the hands of a clock. At the winter solstice, the sun sets as the shadow of the menhir of Row 3 aligns with its stone row.

Drizzlecombe Row 1 with winter solstice shadow alignment.
Explanation: Just before sunset on 17 December 2001 I visited Row 1 where this photograph was taken at about 3.40pm. It shows the shadow of the terminal menhir of Row 1 aligning with its stone row a few minutes before sunset when the light dimmed and became tinted pink. Prior to this Row 2 had aligned the shadow of its terminal menhir with its stone row. A few minutes after the Row 1 alignment, Row 3 aligned as the light became weak and the sun began to set.

Drizzlecombe Row 1 with summer solstice shadow alignment.
Explanation: This photograph shows the menhir of Row 3 and was taken at 2.45pm (five hours before sunset) on 17 June 2002. An alignment with the sun takes place every day producing a shadow (weather permitting) whose length is a maximum at the winter solstice (21 December) and a minimum at the summer solstice (21 June).

These photographs show how the length of the shadow varies according to the time of year.

Row 1 Menhir from the south-east.
Explanation: The metre-length of a walking pole indicates both the size and the aesthetic qualities of the menhir.

The solstices are thought to have had great significance for the people (farmers?) who built the monument, and the day of the winter solstice may have been predicted and measured in two ways. The first by marking the daily positions of the shadow along Row 1 to find the maximum shadow length, which occurs at the winter solstice. The second by observing the sun setting at the time of its alignment with Row 3. The length of the shadow at its daily alignment may also have been used as a calendar to indicate graphically the time of year.

This ancient monument reminds one of how the rising winter solstice sun at Newgrange, in Ireland, is reported to shine briefly down the inlet tunnel into its burial chamber, signifying the start of a new year, or new life.[1]

The Drizzlecombe stone rows may have used the setting sun and shadows at winter solstice to achieve much the same effect, with the shadow of the terminal menhirs pointing along the shadows of the smaller stones to the cairns or burial mounds. The winter solstice alignments may have been intended as graphic fertility symbols, promising life after death and the birth of a new year. The old sun had died and a new sun was to be born.

It appears that the three stone rows act together sequentially to indicate the arrival of the winter solstice sunset, and if ceremonial use was intended, Row 2 may have marked the start of the proceedings.

There are two other solstice alignments built into the Drizzlecombe complex that I hope to investigate, one for summer solstice sunrise, the other for winter solstice sunrise.[2, 3]

Chapter Six

MERRIVALE

Merrivale's Double Stone Rows

Merrivale is an easily accessible part of Dartmoor, to the north of the river Walkham and 7km east of Tavistock on the B3357 road to Princetown. It may be reached by a 15-minute walk from one of the two car parks on the south side of the road about 1km towards Princetown from the Dartmoor Inn at Merrivale.

Merrivale's ancient ceremonial complex straddles the whale-backed ridge of a raised plateau at OS grid reference SX554747. From here it commands sweeping views over the valley of the river Walkham, which extend as far as Plymouth Sound where the waters of the English Channel may be glimpsed on a fine day.

The Merrivale double rows.
Explanation: This is a general view of the plateau and the two double stone rows, showing the two blocking stones and the ridge on the northern horizon with Middle Staple Tor to the west (left) of Great Staple Tor. It is taken looking north-west from the southern row's blocking stone and shows Middle Staple Tor's prominent notch.

Looking west through the double rows.

Looking from the southern row's blocking stone to a figure at the western end of the northern row.

Explanation: The figure (person) standing at the end of the northern double row is due west of the southern row's eastern blocking stone. This east-to-west sight line is an important feature of the rows. It gives the direction of the equinoctial sunset when viewed from the southern row's blocking stone. From here the equinox sun sets on the ridge above the figure (not far from the Pork Hill car park). It is useful to note the position of the equinox sunset on the ridge for some of the following photographs taken at the equinox.

One of the hut circles to the north of the double rows with Great Mis Tor in the background.
Explanation: The valley of the river Walkham to the north of the Merrivale double rows contains many hut circles.

The Merrivale stone circle and standing stone.
Explanation: South of the west end of the southern double row lies the stone circle and standing stone with King's Tor in the background.

The Merrivale menhir looking north-west towards the notch in Middle Staple Tor.

Summer Solstice

One perfect evening, whilst watching the summer solstice sunset at Merrivale, I noticed that the two pointed standing stones (blocking stones), which block the eastern ends of the two double rows, moved towards alignment with the sun as it set behind the ridge between Middle Staple Tor and Great Staple Tor.

As the sun set, it cast the long pointed shadow of the northern row's blocking stone in the direction of the southern row's blocking stone.

Blocking stone summer solstice sunset shadow.
Explanation: This shows the shadow of the northern blocking stone extending towards the southern blocking stone just before summer solstice sunset.

Note: This photograph was taken a few minutes before sunset in order to show the shadow clearly. As sunset approaches, the shadow continues to move clockwise around the northern blocking stone, lengthening and becoming less dense as the light decreases. The leat and its reeds, which distort the shadow, was absent when the double rows were built.

The eastern ends of the two double rows.

The eastern blocking stones and Staple Tor Ridge.

Summer solstice sunset shadow alignment position from the northern double row.
Explanation: This shows the shadow of someone standing at the eastern end of the northern double row at summer solstice sunset, positioned so that their shadow points to the southern row's eastern blocking stone.

In 2000BC the sun would have set 0.93 degrees further north along the ridge. The shadow of a person standing in the northern row close to its blocking stone would then be directly aligned with the southern row's blocking stone.

The design of the northern row allows someone to position themself in the row with their sunset shadow pointing to the southern row's eastern blocking stone at all dates from the spring equinox (21 March) through the summer solstice (21 June) and on to the autumn equinox (23 September). By marking their position in the row, which is 650 feet long, it is possible to know the time of year (the date).

Left: *The summer solstice sun sets on Staple Tor Ridge.*
Explanation: The summer solstice sun sets on Staple Tor Ridge when viewed from the southern row's eastern blocking stone.

Below: *Watching the summer solstice sunset.*
Explanation: People gather at the southern row's eastern blocking stone to experience the monument mark the summer solstice sunset position on Staple Tor Ridge and in the northern double row as it did for its ancient builders four thousand or so years ago.

Photographs of Merrivale's Summer Solstice Sunset taken on 22 June 2005

As summer solstice approaches at Merrivale the photographer's long shadow extends towards the southern double row's blocking stone.

Merrivale's summer solstice sun sets behind Staple Tor ridge.

Merrivale's summer solstice sun sets in the prominent notch on Staple Tor ridge when viewed from the marker stone north of the stone circle.

Twenty-nine minutes after the sun has set at Merrivale it may be observed setting again behind Brent Tor church when viewed from Cox Tor car park (about a kilometre away).

Winter Solstice – The Southern Double Row

Looking west along the southern row from its eastern blocking stone.
Explanation: To the left of the blocking stone is a stone which casts its shadow on the blocking stone at winter solstice sunset, this is the gnomon. Further to the left (south) is the split capstone that covers a cist (stone-box grave). The capstone bears marks where a farmer is reported to have cut a gatepost from the centre.

At a previous winter solstice sunset I had photographed the effect of the setting sun's shadow on the southern row's eastern blocking stone.

Blocking stone and gnomon.
Explanation: A close up view of the southern row's eastern blocking stone and its winter solstice gnomon.

Stones at the west end of the southern double row.
Explanation: The western end of the southern double row is held open by these two standing stones.

The standing stone and the stone circle from the southern row's eastern blocking stone.
Explanation: The standing stone and stone circle lie south-west of the southern row's blocking stone.

The standing stone and circle in winter.
Explanation: The uncovered stone, which is shown here to the north of the circle, is in the current position from which the sun will appear to set in the prominent notch of Middle Staple Tor at the summer solstice (see lower left photograph p.64).

Winter Solstice Sunset

At a previous winter solstice sunset I had photographed the effect of the setting sun's shadow on the southern row's eastern blocking stone.

Right: *Winter solstice sunset shadow 1.*
Explanation: This shows the effect of the winter solstice sun a few minutes before sunset when the light is bright and the shadow of the adjacent stone (the winter solstice gnomon) creeps across the face of the southern row's eastern blocking stone. This shadow appears for a few weeks either side of the winter solstice, becoming central and tallest at the winter solstice sunset. At the solstice, when the shadow reaches the centre of the blocking stone, it glows pink and fades away as the sun sets.

Below: *Winter solstice sunset shadow 2.*
Explanation: Winter solstice light becomes pink at sunset.

Winter solstice sunset.
Explanation: Winter solstice sunset viewed from the northern row's eastern blocking stone.

Scale map of Merrivale's two double rows.
Explanation: From the map there is an obvious alignment with the setting sun and the rows at the equinoxes which are marked '1' and '3'. The map is annotated to show key annual sunset positions and the sun sets due west only at the two equinoxes.

Over a year the sunset angle changes by 80 degrees at Merrivale's 50 degrees latitude when viewed from a given point such as one of the blocking stones, a fact that I shall attempt to show may have been put to good use at this important Dartmoor site.

Merrivale's Sunset Calendar

Realising that the two double rows have alignments with the setting sun at the turning points of the year (the solstices) I constructed a scale map to see if there were any other significant alignments.

Key:
Direction of sunset positions: spring equinox '1' to summer solstice '2' to autumn equinox '3'

Direction of sunset positions: autumn equinox '3' to winter solstice '5' to spring equinox '1'

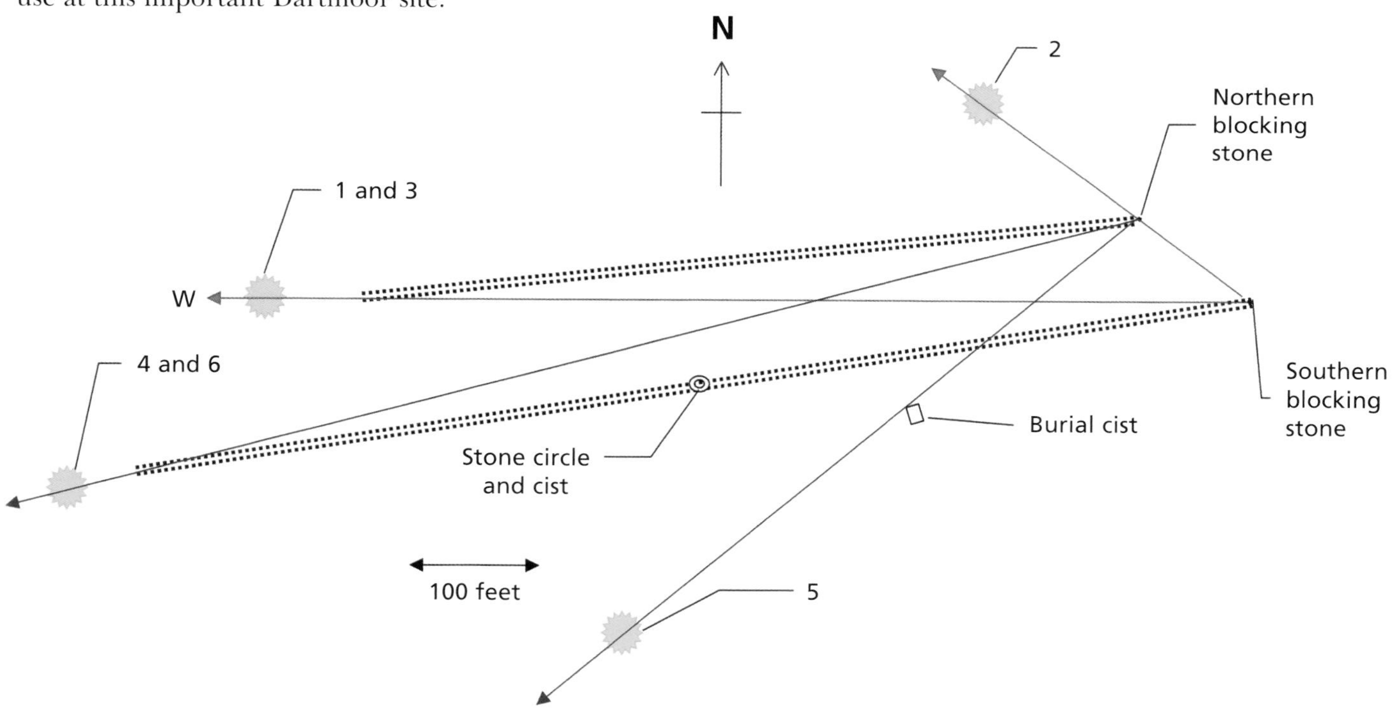

Key dates in the Solar year:
Spring equinox: 21 March, when day and night are of equal length and the year is moving towards summer. Sunset position (due west) marked '1' on the map when viewed from the southern blocking stone.

Summer solstice: 21 June, when the sun is at its highest and daylight lasts for 16 hours. Sunset position '2' on the map when viewed from the southern blocking stone.

Autumn equinox: 23 September, when day and night are of equal length and the year is moving towards winter. Sunset position (due west) position '3' on the map when viewed from the southern blocking stone.

Winter solstice: 21 December, when the sun is at its lowest and daylight lasts for 8 hours. Sunset position '5' on the map when viewed from the northern blocking stone.

Note: When viewed from the northern blocking stone the setting sun will align with positions '4' and '6' on the map at about 19 October and 25 February.

After studying the map a purpose for the double rows suggested itself and the more I thought about it the better it fitted in with their overall design and placement. The summer solstice alignment gave the first clue, the winter solstice alignment supported it, and the precise alignment at the equinoxes (see pp.72–74) confirmed it.

I concluded that the two rows were possibly constructed to enable their designers to record (mark) the daily position of the sun inside them at sunset throughout the year. If so this would have given them a practical, effective and useful calendar, an extremely valuable aid to the management of the lives of these early Dartmoor farmers. I tried the rows at sunset to test the theory and found them easy to use.

Principle

Merrivale's site, with its long east/west double stone rows makes an effective observation/recording platform for marking sunset positions. From this information it is possible to:

(i) Tell the time of the year.

(ii) To predict when the solstices and equinoxes will occur and record/identify/mark these together with any other important dates.

Overall – From the Spring Equinox to the Autumn Equinox

Using the blocking stone at the eastern end of the southern row as a sight throughout and looking towards the setting sun:

Spring equinox sunset.
Explanation: This photograph was taken on 22 March not the 21st and the sunset is therefore a little north of true west.

At the spring equinox the sun sets due west. It sets in line with the western end of the northern double row where the sun's position is marked '1' on the map (due west of the blocking stone sight). It is recorded that the western end of the northern double row also originally ended at a blocking stone.[1]

On the following evening (22 March) the sun will set aligned a little further to the east in the northern row. This new alignment is marked in the northern double row (a little further east along the row).

Sunset shadows on the southern row's eastern blocking stone at the spring equinox.
Explanation: The first two eastern stones on the north side of the southern row cast their sunset shadows on the row's eastern blocking stone, reminiscent of that of the gnomon at winter solstice sunset.

This procedure is repeated each day (weather permitting) until at the summer solstice the sun's setting direction is marked inside the northern row's eastern blocking stone at position '2' on the map, whose shadow then points towards the southern row's eastern blocking stone.

After the summer solstice the sun's setting position daily moves westward and its alignment may continue to be marked in the northern row until the autumn equinox.

Autumn equinox sunset.
Explanation: At the autumn equinox the sun sets due west of the southern row's eastern blocking stone, aligning with the western end of the northern row and appearing to set on the highest part of Barn Hill ridge, not far from Pork Hill car park.

Knowing the position and direction of movement of the setting sun as marked in the northern row indicates the time of year (date) from the spring equinox on 21 March until the autumn equinox on 23 September each year.

When I tested the practicality of marking sunset positions in the northern double row, I found that one person may do this easily as follows:

Walk along the northern row at sunset until your long shadow points to the southern row's eastern blocking stone. Then place a marker in the row at this position (possibly by rolling a suitable stone along the row). The position of the marker in the row and its direction of movement indicate the time of year.

Finding the position of the setting sun in the northern double row.

Explanation: At any time of year from the spring equinox until the autumn equinox there is a position in the northern row at sunset where the elongated shadow of a person standing in the row points to the southern row's eastern blocking stone. This position is easily found and marked to show the time of the year (the date). For everyday purposes it would be more practical to mark sunset positions in the rows than to have numerous large markers on the horizon. One might also conjecture that bringing the sun's positional information on to tribal land may have inferred control over the sun and enhanced ceremonial activities.

The following paragraph outlines a method for finding the solstices more accurately.

Take any sunset alignment position along the row (say at a particular stone) and count the number of sunsets that it takes to pass from here through the solstice and back to the same (particular stone) sunset position. Half of this number is the number of days (sunsets) from this stone to the solstice. This method may also have been used to predict the time of the solstice from shadow positions at Hingston Hill and other sites.

As indicated above, using the southern row's eastern blocking stone as a sight, the northern row is perfectly aligned to allow the positions of the sun to be marked inside the row at any sunset from the spring equinox (position '1' on the map – p70), through the summer solstice (position '2' on the map – p70), back to the autumn equinox (position '3' on the map – p70).

From the autumn equinox the setting sun daily moves progressively south along the western horizon until it reaches position '4' on the map. From here, using the northern row's blocking stone as a sight, the positions of the sun at sunset may be recorded in the southern row, until the winter solstice when the sun sets at position '5'. After the solstice the daily setting sun moves back through position '6' to the next spring equinox at position '1' from where the annual cycle repeats.

As described above the southern double row comes into alignment with the setting sun at position '4' on the map on about 19 October, before the winter solstice and again on 22 February after the winter solstice. Similarly the small stone circle which is almost in the middle of the southern row aligns about 30 October and again on 11 February.[2]

The southern horizon is not so sharply defined as the northern one for plotting sunset positions, which may explain why there are several raised mounds (now all but destroyed) just to the south of the southern double row. These may each have been placed to form artificial horizons behind which the sun set at key times of the year. For example there was a cairn over the burial cist.[3] (See diagram – p.70).

The top of this burial mound may have been constructed to align with the northern row's blocking stone to cause the sun to set behind it. Or perhaps as described at Hingston Tor in Chapter 4 behind a person standing on top of the mound at winter solstice sunset, with their long shadow reaching towards the northern row's eastern blocking stone.

Finding the sunset position from the southern row.
Explanation: The long sunset shadow points at the northern row's blocking stone, indicating the sunset position in the row and hence the time of year.

Conclusions for the Double Rows:
A calendar of the type described here, based on the turning points of the year (the solstices) has a beautiful utility. It is easy to maintain and read whilst providing its early Dartmoor builders with adequate accuracy for following and planning their farming year.[4] It may also have added visual impact to ceremonies linked to the solstices, equinoxes and to other dates. We may suppose that much was made of the setting, calibration and reading of such a device.

Due to the remarkable preservation of the Merrivale double rows and the fact that the sun's position relative to the Earth has not significantly changed over the last 4000 years, we may assume that the rows' alignments with the sun are close to their original settings. Put simply: *After approximately 4000 years of service Merrivale's double stone rows continue to faithfully display the time of year, the solstices and the equinoxes.*

Having established this system for recording and predicting information based on the sun to improve their lives. It could be surmised that these early Dartmoor farmers would look for further help from the heavens, plotting the positions of the moon and possibly some stars to assist them with their quest for control over their environment and the increased sustenance this may provide.

Chapter Seven

Some Ancient Sun Calendars

Throughout the ancient world there is strong evidence to show that the sun's position was recorded to tell the time of the year and co-ordinate human social, spiritual and physical needs.

If the Dartmoor monuments considered here were the only ones to have rather obvious alignments to the sun, it would be easy to dismiss them as coincidental.

However there is much to link many ancient monuments with sun alignments. Here is a short list of ancient European sun calendars together with their locations. They will be compared with the Dartmoor monuments:

Stonehenge	Southern Britain
The Nebra Sky Disk	Germany
'Uriel's Machine'	Europe & Mediterranean Areas

Stonehenge

First impressions suggest that Dartmoor's ancient monuments have little in common with the overwhelming majesty of Stonehenge, which is designated by UNESCO as a World Heritage site. However when we ask, 'What was the purpose of Stonehenge?' Some common factors emerge which tell us that the monuments may not be so different after all. By comparing Stonehenge with the Dartmoor monuments, it may be possible to infer more of their original use(s) than by considering each location in isolation.

Stonehenge is probably Britain's most famous prehistoric monument. For more than five thousand years it has endured at the heart of a fertile plain in England's bountiful southern region, inspiring all those who have seen it. There is something uplifting in the way that light plays upon its raised monoliths, changing their colours, linking earth to sky, through stone.

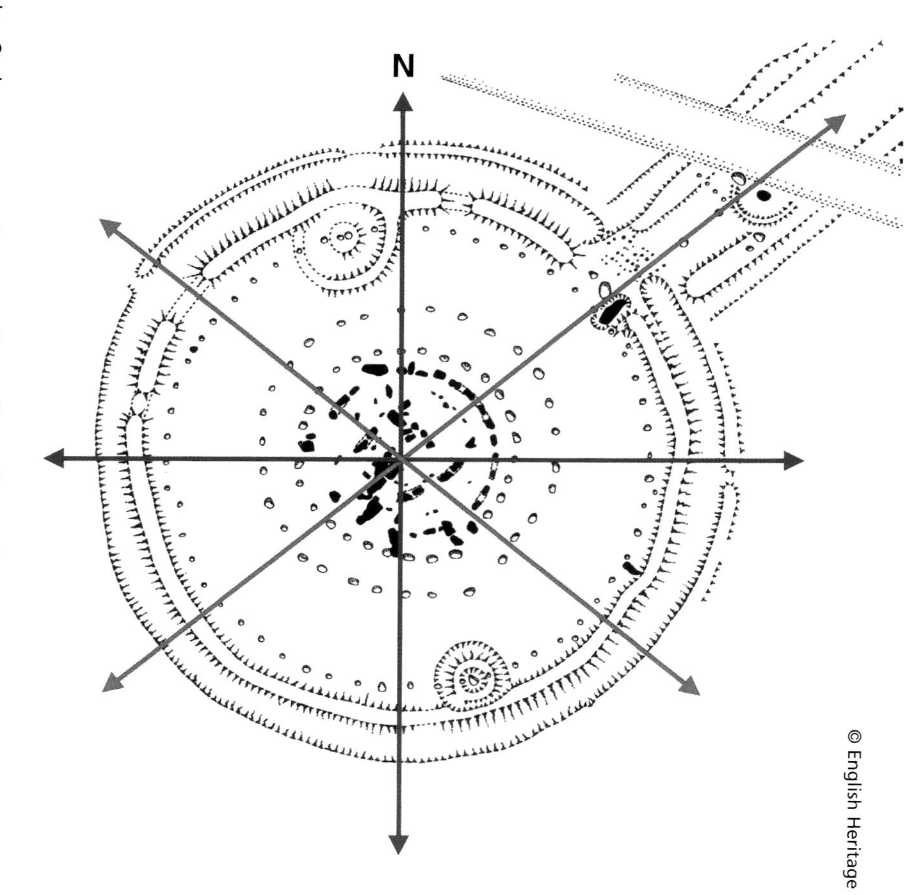

Plan of Stonehenge.

Key:

The plan is in black and white.
The A303 road is shown to the north-east.
Existing stones are shown filled in black.
The positions of missing stones are shown as outlines.
The heelstone is the large black shape close to the A303 and the north-east red (summer solstice sunrise) line. Note: There were two heelstones, one each side of the summer solstice sunrise red line.

Additions to the plan:

The blue lines are drawn to indicate north, south, east and west from the centre.
The red lines from the centre:
- to the north-east indicates summer solstice sunrise alignment.
- to the south-east indicates winter solstice sunrise alignment.
- to the south-west indicates winter solstice sunset alignment.
- to the north-west indicates summer solstice sunset alignment.

The blue line pointing east from the centre indicates the direction of the spring and autumn equinox sunrise.
The blue line pointing west from the centre indicates the direction of the spring and autumn equinox sunset.

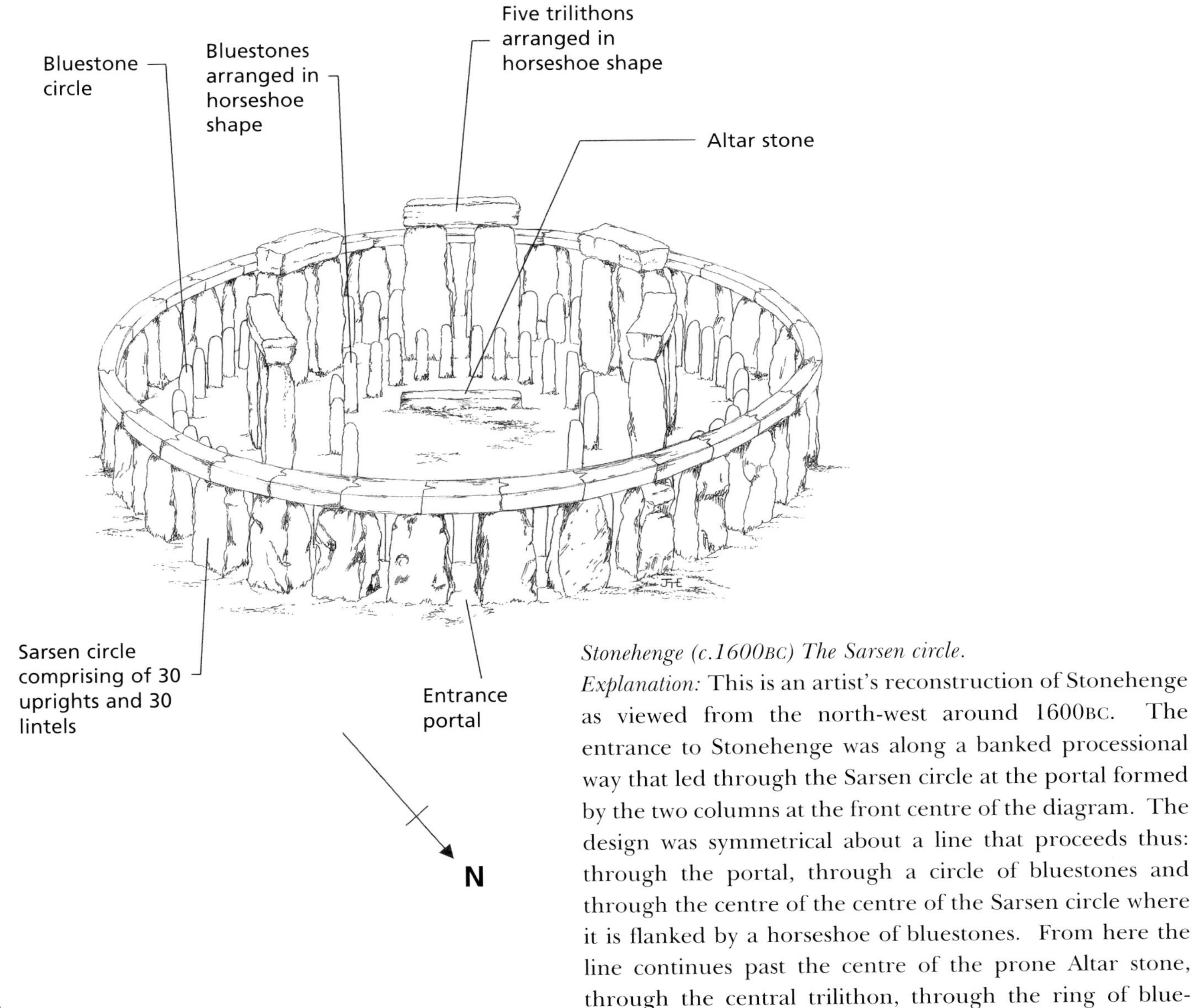

Stonehenge (c.1600BC) The Sarsen circle.

Explanation: This is an artist's reconstruction of Stonehenge as viewed from the north-west around 1600BC. The entrance to Stonehenge was along a banked processional way that led through the Sarsen circle at the portal formed by the two columns at the front centre of the diagram. The design was symmetrical about a line that proceeds thus: through the portal, through a circle of bluestones and through the centre of the centre of the Sarsen circle where it is flanked by a horseshoe of bluestones. From here the line continues past the centre of the prone Altar stone, through the central trilithon, through the ring of bluestones, and out of the Sarsen circle on the far side.

Stonehenge from the north-east.
Explanation: The central portal shown here gives an impression of the imposing sight faced by visitors to Stonehenge around 1600BC as they followed the processional way into the great circle of 30 Sarsen columns connected by 30 curved lintels.

Stonehenge from the south-west.
Explanation: This photograph is annotated to identify some of the main elements of Stonehenge.

Stonehenge from the Slaughter-stone.
Explanation: This shows the full Sarsen circle from the north-west with the Slaughter-stone in the foreground. The central axis goes through the entrance portal, past the central trilithon, whose tenon is seen in the background above the entrance lintel.

Stonehenge from the Heel-stone.
Explanation: This shows the monument from the Heel-stone, which is a few metres south of the line of the central axis that passes through the monument, unobstructed except for the prone Altar stone. The central axis follows the line of the summer solstice sunrise from the north-west horizon near the Heel-stone to the winter solstice sunset position, which appears framed in the entrance portal on the south-west horizon on the far side of the monument.

The Solstice Axis.
Explanation: Framed in the entrance portal to the north-east is the dimpled shape of the Heel-stone. The monument's central axis goes through the monument, past the edges of the central trilithon in the near foreground and the Sarsen in the foreground.

Stonehenge Today

The construction of Stonehenge began around 3000BC although there are indications of some kind of use of the site back as far as 7000BC. The Stonehenge that we see today is the remains of the original monument after fourteen hundred years of development, followed by its abandonment around 1600BC.

Description of the main features

Inside the 30-metre diameter of the Sarsen circle stood five trilithons. The gap between the uprights of the tallest trilithon is on the axis of the monument and aligned to allow the passage of the rising summer solstice sun and the setting winter solstice sun to shine through its uprights. The other four trilithons are arranged in a horseshoe with two each side of the path of the rising solstice sun, as if to guide it into the monument.

Arranged inside the trilithon horseshoe was another horseshoe of bluestones. Between the Sarsen circle and the trilithon horseshoe was a circle of bluestones. Standing or lying at the foot of the gap between the uprights of the tallest trilithon and in front of the bluestone horseshoe was a sandstone block the, Altar stone.

On the same centre as the 15-metre radius Sarsen circle, but with radiuses a few metres outside this, are two circles of filled-in post-holes. Closest are the 30 'Z Holes' with a radius of about 19 metres. Beyond these, with a radius of about 26 metres, are the 30 'Y Holes'. Both the roughly equally spaced 'Z Holes' and 'Y Holes' were arranged so as not to block the path of the monument's central axis. The so-called Aubrey Holes are on the same centre at a radius of about 42 metres.

The henge itself is a circular ditch at a radius of about 57 metres from the centre of the monument. From the inner edge of the ditch was a circular bank.

Summer solstice sunrise simulation over the Heel-stone.

Explanation: This shows a simulation of the summer solstice sun rising over the existing heelstone as viewed through the monument along the central axis. The long shadow of the Heel-stone would project close to, and parallel with, the axis of the monument.

Significant summer solstice sunrise shadows.
Explanation: This shows the shadows of both of the Heel-stones pointing along the processional way to the entrance portal of Stonehenge at summer solstice sunrise. Inside the entrance the uprights of the entrance portal point their parallel shadows over the Altar stone.

Note: *There is a socket for a large stone a little to the north of and slightly behind the Heel-stone, which is thought to have contained a second Heel-stone. The shadows of the two Heel-stones would have lined each side of the processional way, much as the uprights of the entrance portal do inside the Sarsen circle.*

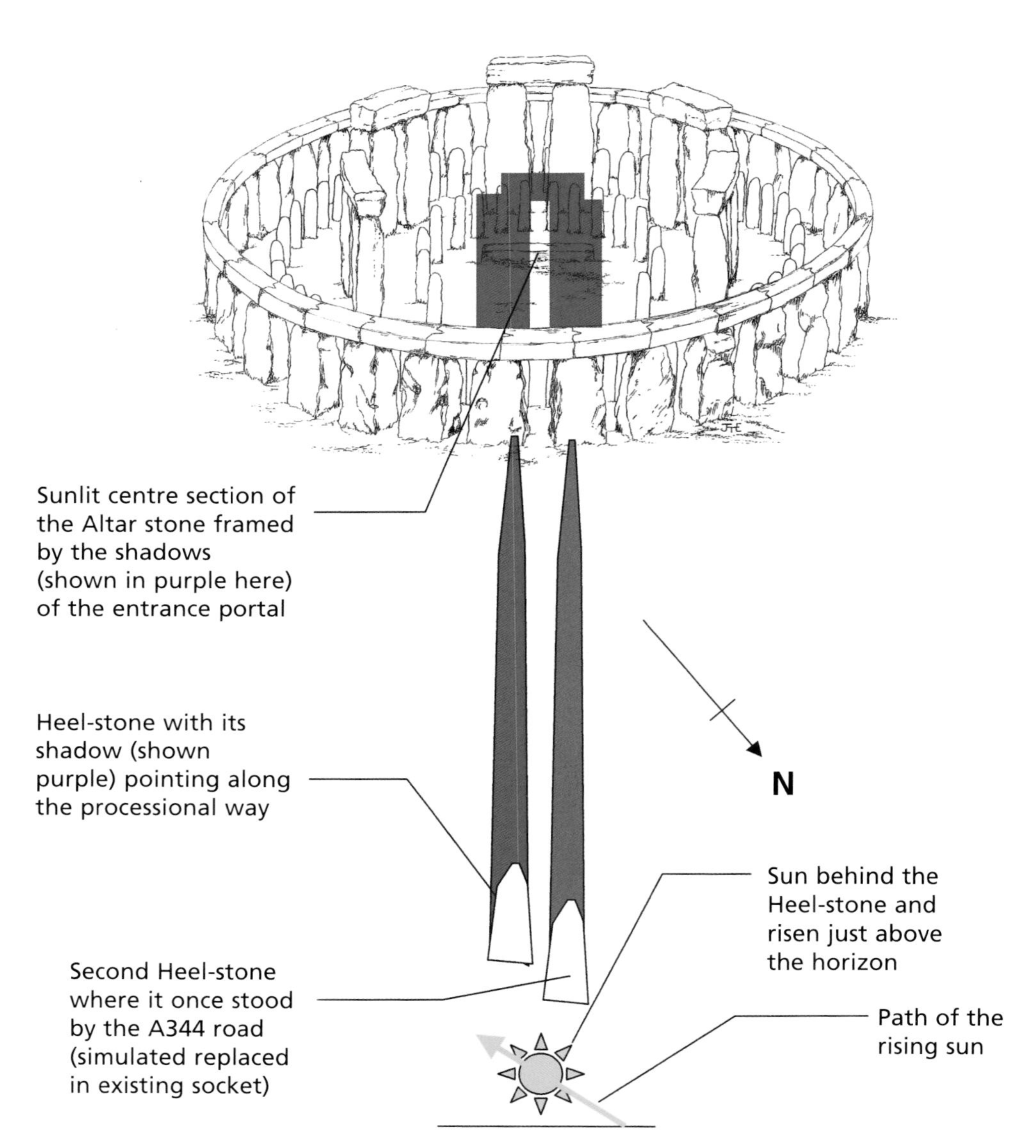

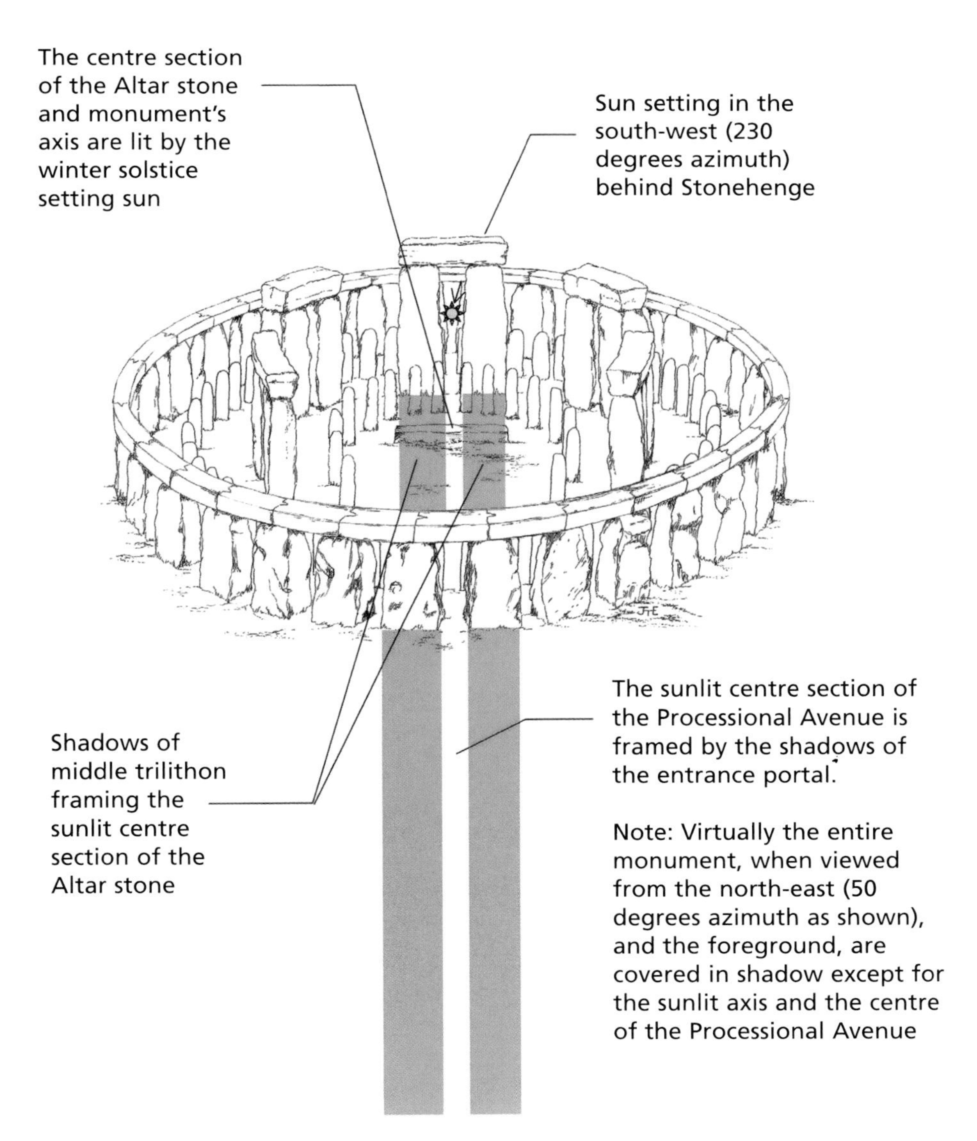

Significant winter solstice sunset shadows.

Explanation: At winter solstice sunset the central trilithon casts the twin shadows of its uprights across the Altar stone and through the entrance portal. From here the twin shadows of the entrance portal uprights extend along either side of the processional way towards the Heel-stones. This effect is almost a repeat of the summer solstice sunrise shadows and appears to be deliberate. It is difficult to resist the conclusion that the monument is fundamentally arranged such that at both solstices the shadows lead along the main axis of the monument, which was the processional way for ceremonial purposes.

The megaliths of Stonehenge exert a world-wide attraction. For each of the last few years around 800 000 people have visited Stonehenge.[1]

It is widely acknowledged that the remains of the final construction from around 1600BC were aligned symmetrically along an axis. This axis pointed to the summer solstice sunrise at the horizon in the north-east (about 50 degrees clockwise from true north) and the winter solstice sunset on the horizon in the south-west (about 50+180=230) degrees clockwise from true north.

Note: In practice the alignments would have been arrived at over many years, with due allowance for imperfections in the levels of the actual horizon. For this reason it is pointless to work out theoretical angles with great accuracy and expect them to be true in practice. The real world isn't like that, which is one of the reasons why it is best to state 'about 50 degrees.'

The theoretical azimuth position of the summer solstice sunrise on a level site at Stonehenge's latitude was 48 degrees, 19 minutes and 18 seconds in 2004BC, and 49 degrees 15 minutes and 24 seconds in AD2004.[2] These values each allow 50 minutes of a degree to compensate for refraction, but are meaningless for practical purposes. The ancient Stonehenge builders simply had to erect two Heel-stones to cast their shadows along the processional way soon after summer solstice sunrise.

The complexity of Stonehenge and its construction suggest that it was a major centre of influence, with the ability to call on a large labour force. Its blue stones quantify its minimum range of influence. The fifty or so blue stones used at Stonehenge originated in the Preseli Hills of South Wales (which are closer to Stonehenge than Dartmoor). *If the people of Stonehenge had sufficient influence to obtain the heavy blue stones and to get them from the Preseli Hills to*

Stonehenge, then it would not be surprising if they also had influence on Dartmoor and indeed over a wider range.

Although Dartmoor does not contain monuments to compare with Stonehenge, examination of the existing Stonehenge monument suggests there are similarities in the technology used at Stonehenge and on Dartmoor to indicate both the solstices and the sun's annual calendar.

It is interesting to note that Dartmoor's Hingston Hill monument has suggested how Stonehenge may have appeared at the solstices and that precise theoretical measurement of the angle of the sun was not required. It is not necessary to know if the monuments were aligned with the top of the sun, or the bottom or the middle, for they come into alignment after the sun has risen above the horizon. A lonely Dartmoor monument on Hingston Hill came into alignment for me in a blaze of summer solstice morning sunlight, as it had for thousands of years, to demonstrate the process.

Stonehenge at 3000BC

In order to illustrate how the Dartmoor monuments fit into a coherent system of important ancient monuments throughout Western Europe, it is also useful to compare them with the Stonehenge of 3000BC.

Around 3000BC Stonehenge consisted simply of a chalk circle and ditch (the henge). Inside the henge were 56 holes, now known as the Aubrey Holes and presumably 56 posts stood in the Aubrey Holes.

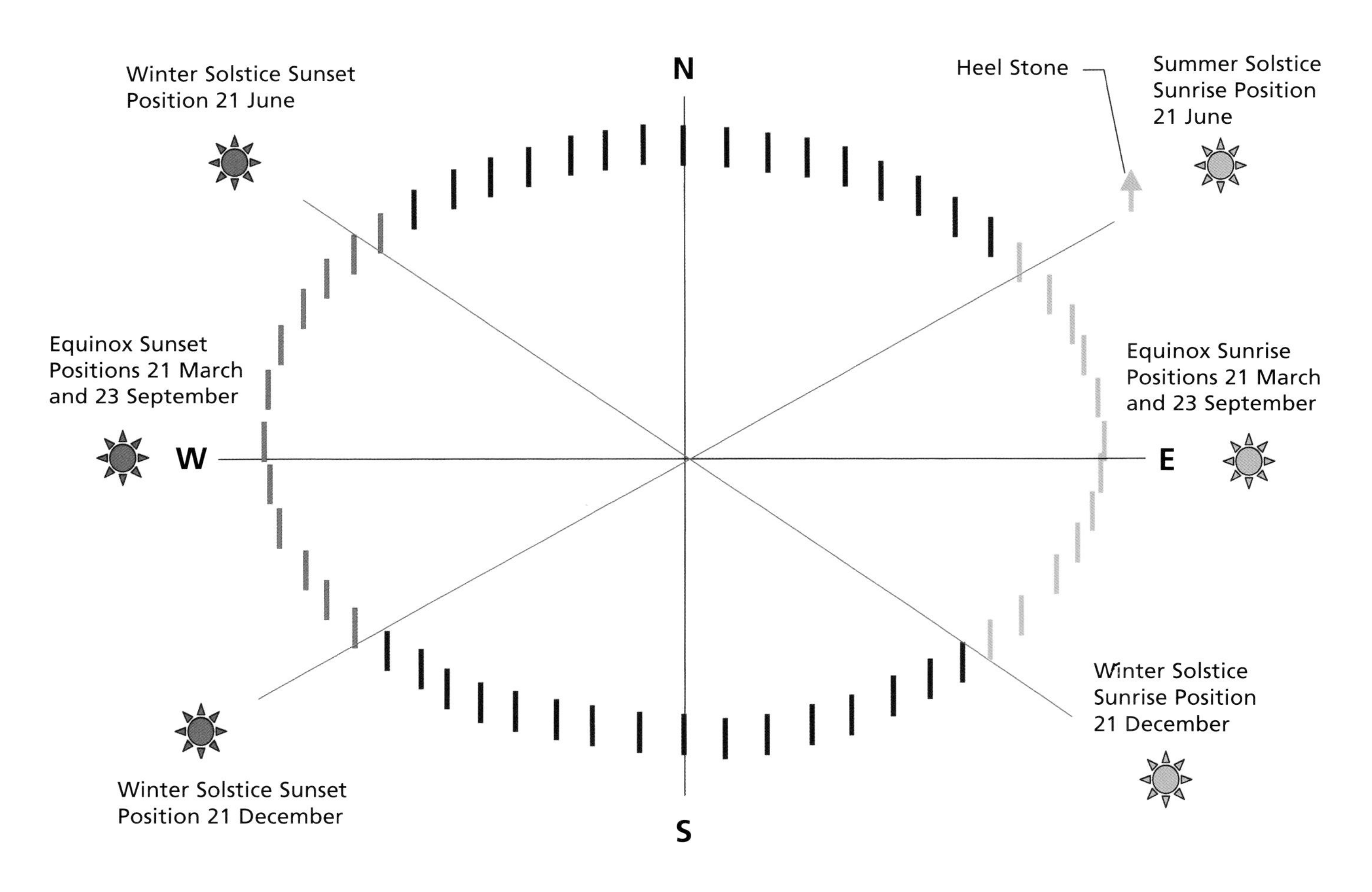

Stonehenge 3000BC – the Aubrey Holes and poles.
Explanation: This system of sunset markers, in one form or another, is a common feature of sun calendars. Shadows of the poles at sunrise and sunset point in turn to the centre of the circle indicating the time of year. An improvement that takes into account the months of the year is shown in 'Uriel's Machine', which is examined later in this chapter.

The Nebra Sky Disk is possibly a variation of the Stonehenge Aubrey Hole sun calendar.

The Nebra Sky Disk (a prehistoric calendar?)

A bronze disk subsequently dated to 1600BC was recently unearthed from the top of wooded Mittleberg Hill near the town of Nebra, which is 180km south-west of Berlin, Germany.

Set with gold circles and arcs, the 32-centimetre diameter disk is currently valued at $18million US. The Nebra Sky Disk is believed to show the positions of the rising and setting sun throughout the year as observed from the top of the Mittleberg Hill, using other prominent hills on the horizon as markers. In particular it is claimed that the positions of summer and winter solstice sunset, together with the equinox sunset position, are marked on the disk and related to positions on the horizon.

It is suggested that the disk is set to this distant horizon to function as a calendar, providing farmers with information critical for planting and harvesting.

Additionally the positions of small gold disks on the Nebra Sky Disk are claimed to make it the oldest accurate depiction of the night sky.

At the bottom of the disc is a golden arc, which is similar to the ancient Egyptian shape for the boat that was supposed to carry the sun on its journey through the underworld. Supporting this assumption is a large sun disk and a moon shape over the boat. To the east is a golden arc covering sunrise positions and to the west another golden arc covering sunset positions.

It is also suggested that the disk may originate from the site of a German equivalent of Stonehenge and:

'The disk which tracks the sun's movement along the horizon, contains the oldest known depiction of the night sky and may have served as an agricultural and spiritual calendar…

'If the Sky Disk could predict celestial events, it would have wielded enormous power to its owner – as did the Pharaohs who could forecast the Nile's annual floods.'[3]

Around the edge of the Sky Disk are a series of holes. It has been suggested these were used for some kind of fastenings, but they have a similar layout to the Stonehenge Aubrey Holes and may possibly have had the same use.

'Uriel's Machine' (a prehistoric calendar?)

The Dead Sea Scrolls are reported to record (amongst many other historic and prehistoric accounts) the description of the design of an ancient calendar. Enoch, a Middle Eastern, Old Testament leader from the Megalithic Period, travelled to a northern land (which may fit the description of Stonehenge) where he met Uriel.

Uriel taught Enoch how to make a device – 'Uriel's Machine' – that would show the positions of the sun at sunrise and sunset throughout the year and was intended for use as a calendar.[4]

'Uriel's Machine' comprised a series of upright posts arranged around the perimeter of a circle, which in their turn cast their shadows at the rise and set of the sun into the centre of a circle to show the month of the year. Smaller divisions between the posts divided the sunrise and sunset positions further, allowing the machine (the moving parts were the shadows) to be used as a calendar.

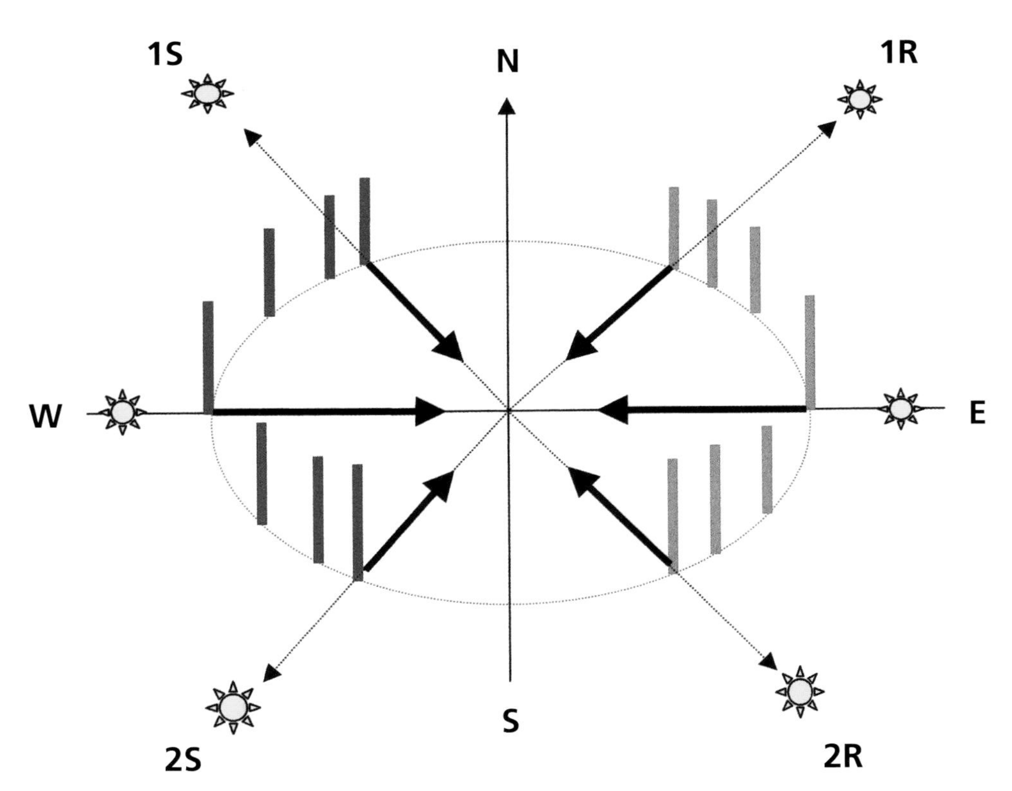

'Uriel's Machine'.

Key:

For clarity two colours of vertical posts are shown here:

Seven blue posts to cast sunset shadows into the circle.

Seven red posts to cast sunrise shadows into the circle.

These shadows are shown here as pointed thick black lines.

1R is the sunrise position at the summer solstice.

1S is the sunset position at the summer solstice.

E is the sunrise position at the autumn and spring equinox.

W is the sunset position at the autumn and spring equinox.

2R is the sunrise position at the winter solstice.

2S is the sunset position at the winter solstice.

Explanation:

At the equinoxes the sun rises due east and sets due west. A sunrise shadow points due west to where the sun will set on that day and the sunset shadow points due east, to where the sun arose, this only occurs at the equinoxes. With care it is possible to place two upright posts so that their shadows align with the rising and setting sun on the same day. This is thought to be one way that the positions of east and west were determined in ancient times.

Each of the four vertical posts, in each quadrant of 'Uriel's Machine' is set 30 days, that is 30 sunsets or sunrises apart. This is thought to be because the year (in ancient Egypt for example) was divided into twelve months of thirty days each, making a (12 times 30 = 360) three-hundred-and-sixty-day year. The other five-and-a-quarter days were discounted and each subsequent year was started again in accordance with alignments with sun, therefore the calendar was self-correcting.

It is thought that the 30-day month (or moonth) is derived from the apparent twenty-nine-and-a-half days that it takes to complete the average period of the moon's cycle as observed from Earth.

The spaces between the vertical posts of 'Uriel's Machine' were divided into smaller graduations with shorter posts between to improve the accuracy of this type of calendar.

With 'Uriel's Machine' the time of year could be determined on any day throughout the year by observing the shadows thrown by both the rising and setting of the sun.

Summary:
Having first marked out a circle and set two posts on its circumference in an east/west axis, further posts marking each month are placed on the circumference of the circle. The result is 'Uriel's Machine', which is in effect a prehistoric calendar, which may be constructed and used to indicate the time of year almost anywhere on land.

Conclusion

The ancient monuments of Dartmoor and Stonehenge, and devices such as Nebra and Uriel, appear to share common technology and possibly a common lineage.

Chapter Eight

Hingston Hill and Merrivale Revisited

Hingston Hill Revisited

Ancient Boundary Work?

Having visited Stonehenge and examined various sun calendars, something about the Hingston Hill monument demanded an answer.

Approximately 100 metres to the west of the monument, an ancient wall follows the shape of the circle continuously through the north-west and south-west. On some OS maps this is marked as an ancient boundary work, but it may have had another purpose.

The ancient wall forms a continuous raised horizon behind which the sun sets throughout the year when viewed from the stone circle. This makes the ancient wall ideal for marking the sun's position at sunset throughout the year. Another 100 metres beyond the ancient wall to the south-west is the high point of Hingston Hill marked by Hingston Tor which is in a direct line with the winter solstice sunset from the circle.

The question was: 'Is this another sun calendar?'

One hard, bright winter's morning in 2004, with the wind blowing cold enough to take our breath away, some friends helped me mark the positions of the 30-day months (moonths) by standing on the ancient wall at the monthly alignment positions.

Winter trees at Norsworthy car park.
Explanation: Stark trees shelter amongst moss lined granite boulders much as they may have done thousands of winters ago.

Winter solstice sunset position.
Explanation: A person stands on the ancient wall in line with the circle, the winter solstice sunset position and Hingston Tor. At winter solstice sunset their shadow would be cast into the circle.

Summer monthly sunset positions.

Explanation: Three people (and a rucksack) stand on the ancient wall at monthly sunset positions. Starting just to the left of the centre horizon, tin miners' pits have scattered the ancient wall here and all that can be seen is the head of the person. This position is due west of the circle and corresponds to the equinox sunset of 21 March. Moving right (north) along the horizon the next position corresponds to sunset on 21 April, the next 21 May, and on finally to the small rucksack on the mound which marks summer solstice sunset on 21 June. Moving south after the summer solstice the next position marks sunset on the 21 July, the next 21 August and then back to the central position again, which now corresponds to the sunset position on 23 September, which is the autumn equinox.

Sunset positions for the entire year.

Explanation: This is taken looking west down the stone row past the circle to the positions marked 1 to 7 on the horizon. The seven markers show the monthly positions of sunsets throughout the year in their true positions when observed from the centre of the circle.

Marker 1 indicates the winter solstice sunset position.
Marker 2 indicates one month before and after winter solstice sunset.
Marker 3 indicates two months before and after winter solstice sunset position.
Marker 4 indicates the spring and autumn equinox sunset positions.
Marker 7 indicates the summer solstice sunset position.
Marker 6 indicates one month before and after summer solstice sunset position.
Marker 5 indicates two months before and after summer solstice sunset position.

It appears that the calendar is designed to be reset to the true winter solstice sunset position by aligning it with the maximum southerly position of the long sunset shadow cast from Hingston Tor.

The ancient wall that curves around the monument provides an ideal artificially raised horizon on which to place uprights (poles or stones) to divide the year into monthly sunset positions and form a calendar.

This evaluation of the monument explains why it is located where it is, some of the functions of its main elements, and some of its uses. It suggests the importance of the solstices to the builders and indicates how they were able to organise their lives based on the positions of the Dartmoor sun.

It is significant to realise that the ancient wall extends beyond the solstice sunset positions, a factor that suggests the builders may have also plotted the setting positions of the moon, the planets and some other stars. However it was the understanding of the sun that gave them control over their environment. Civilisation followed.

Merrivale Revisited

There is no absolute reason why the sunset position posts of a 'Uriel Machine' have to be set on a circle. Providing there is a fixed observation point on an east-to-west axis, the sunset marking posts may just as well run in a straight line. This appears to be the situation at Merrivale where the northern double row replaces the sunset marking posts and the user positions him- or herself in the row until their shadow points at the southern row's eastern blocking stone at sunset. The users' position in the row indicates the time of year from the spring equinox to the autumn equinox, with the user being in effect the gnomon. The extensive length of the northern row assures good accuracy and fits the design to the site, avoiding the complications of constructing a circle of similar radius. As described previously, the eastern blocking stone of the northern row may then be used as the sight for winter shadows using the southern row to mark the position of the setting sun.

The Wider, Older(?) Merrivale Complex

Although Merrivale's double stone rows may be its most prominent features there are other items of interest.

There is a profusion of ruined cairns and fallen stones, together with a stone circle and an impressive standing stone.

Merrivale may have developed over an extended period, in much the same way as Stonehenge. The antiquities lying south of the double rows are of a more simple construction than the double rows, which suggests an earlier date.

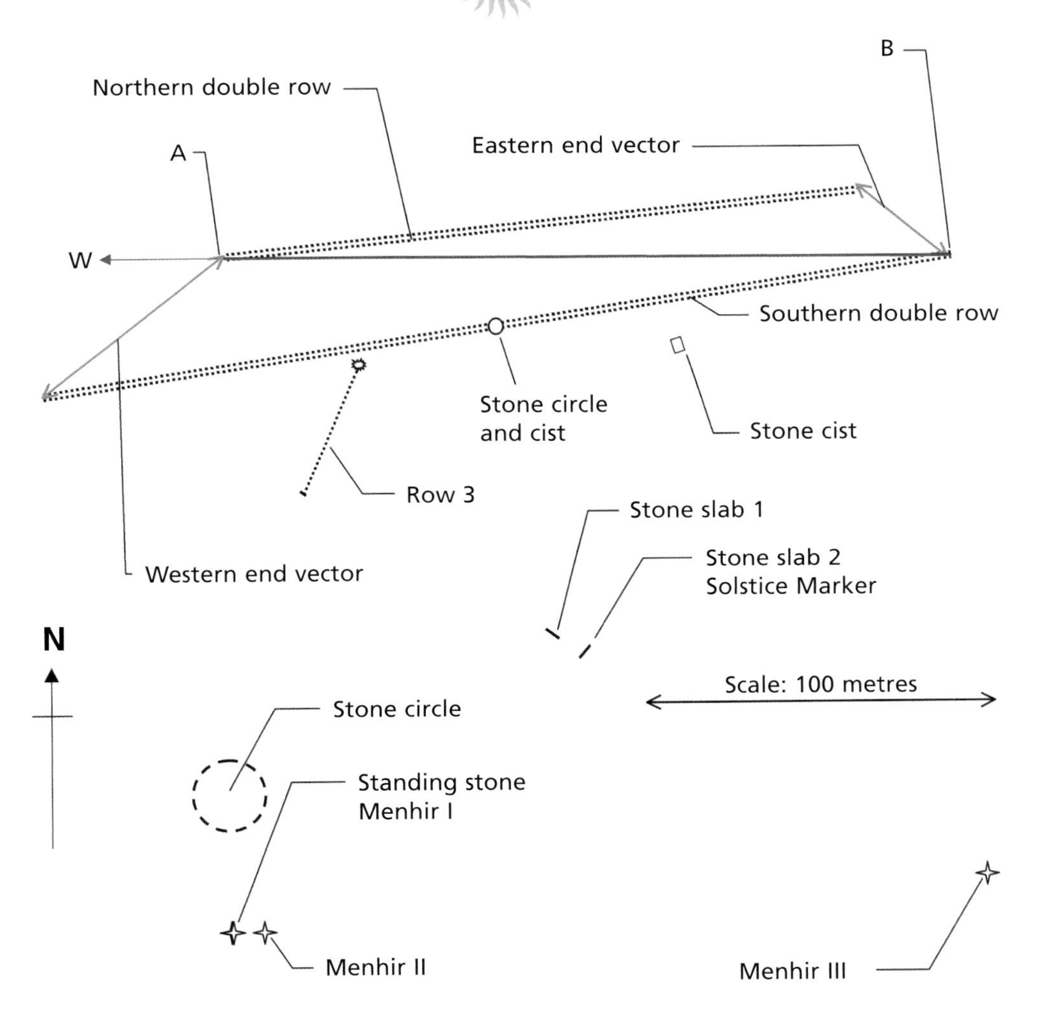

Merrivale – sketch of obvious features.
Explanation: This shows the positions of some features of the Merrivale complex that have survived in good condition. There are others in various states with further items perhaps lying unnoticed. There are also the remains of a single stone row (Row 3) together with overgrown circles or cists a few metres south of the southern row along its western end.

The Double Row's Eastern and Western End Vectors

The lines joining the ends of the rows, which are marked in blue on the diagram (p103) are labelled as the 'Eastern and Western end vectors' and align with the turning points of the solstice sun. The eastern end vector points 310 degrees to the setting summer solstice sun and 130 degrees to the rising winter solstice sun. And the western end vector points 50 degrees to the rising summer solstice sun and 230 degrees to the setting winter solstice sun.

South Merrivale's Older Technology?

There is the suggestion that the double rows were constructed following an earlier sun-based system located to south of them.

South Merrivale's Summer Solstice Sunset Alignment

A respected scientist reported:
'*From the centre of the flattened circle* (annotated 'Stone Circle' on diagram p.103), *the solstitial sun would have set behind the prominent notch in Middle Staple Tor in the Late Neolithic and Early Bronze* Ages…'[1]

South Merrivale's Winter Solstice Sunset Alignment

Winter solstice simulation.

Explanation: This shows the simulated setting winter solstice sun as it aligns with the 3 metres high Menhir 1 and the Winter Solstice Sunset Marker (which is shown as 'Stone slab 2' on the diagram on p103). The stone to the right is 'Stone slab 1' on that diagram.

'Stone slab 1' is very unusual. It has a circular hole through its top and is set across a sight line half way between the standing stone and the southern double row's eastern blocking stone.

Stone slab 1.

Explanation: The unusual feature of the hole through the slab is all the more interesting as the hole aligns with Menhir 1, which is shown in the distance pointing to the horizon near where the winter solstice sun presently sets. At about 2000BC the sunset would have been around 0.93 degrees closer to this alignment. Was this the original winter solstice sunset alignment?

Standing stone menhir 1 before winter solstice sunset alignment.
Explanation: A few minutes before the winter solstice sunset the shadow of the Menhir 1 slowly rotates clockwise, passing Stone slab 1 on its way to the Solstice Marker Stone (Stone slab 2).

Merrivale winter solstice sun sets behind the southern row's blocking stone.

Merrivale's winter solstice sun sets behind Menhir 1 as viewed from the solstice marker stone.

Explanation: It is necessary to remember the splendid visual effect of the winter solstice sunset that marks the end of the old year and the beginning of the new.

Chapter Nine

Life on Prehistoric Dartmoor

At some time in the Neolithic or Bronze Age, possibly from the second or third millennium BC people made settlements on areas of Dartmoor and began to farm. They cleared land of the broadleaf forest that covered all but the highest parts of the moor and supplemented their hunting by husbanding animals and growing grain. It was inevitable that they began to identify with the land and sought to understand it. They came to understand the rhythms of the earth and the sky and followed their cyclic changes. Now they were settled they had to devise ways to organise and co-ordinate their activities with their physical and spiritual needs. Stone burial chambers were constructed to protect their dead. Monuments were erected aligned with the sun to inform them and their descendants of the seasons and the time of the year.

Prehistoric Reeves and Fields

There are few, if any, fortified sites on Dartmoor before the Iron Age, which suggests that the people lived peacefully.

The moor's many ancient monuments are testament to a strong spiritual component in these ancient peoples' lives.

Dartmoor is criss-crossed by low walls called reeves, which must have taken a huge effort to construct. Fanning out from the reeves are small but carefully laid out field structures. Work of this nature and magnitude suggests a cohesive social structure. Although it is difficult to date the construction of the reeves, some are thought to date back at least to the second or third millennium BC.

Those who followed the early settlers respected their monuments for more than two millennia, which again suggests they lived peaceful lives without fear or resentment.

Round Houses

Hundreds of hut circles, many of which are the remains of round houses, nestle in the moor, some in groups of two or three, others in villages; some in walled enclosures, others not. The huts had thick stone walls with high thatched roofs and doors facing to the south, but the occupants appear to have made an effort not to overlook each other.

A typical hut had an inside diameter of 5 to 7 metres, giving it about the same living area as a Victorian farm cottage.[1]

In the centre of the paved or beaten floor of some of the round houses was a hearth, and around the walls 'beds' were built with stone kerbs, possibly to keep fresh grass or heather sleeping material neatly contained.

I recently visited a round house that was constructed two years ago on private land. It was built as a labour of love after much study of the remains of many of Dartmoor's prehistoric round houses. The builders followed the same construction patterns and used the same materials wherever possible as the prehistoric builders. It was suggested that this hut is towards the larger size of round house found on the moor and I estimated the interior diameter to be about 7 metres. Variation in hut size is an indication that they were designed for different purposes. Those with large diameters and a central hearth may have been for communal use.

There was a storm raging as I followed the owners past a medieval barn into a drenched grassy field, to where the round house nestled into the landscape, impervious to the weather. Its dry-stone granite wall was topped by a steeply thatched golden cone roof that overhung the base, keeping it dry. Two granite posts lifted the lintel a little above the walls to form a doorway, and the entrance approach was paved with stone, as was the immediate interior when we ducked inside through the low doorway.

By the light of a few candles we moved past a circle of stout posts to stand beside a stone hearth. The point of the roof was six and half metres above the floor level creating an impression of space, similar to that of a small church hall.

Around the wall the floor was paved about a quarter of the way to the middle, with the remainder surfaced in hard-packed earth that led to a small paved area around the central square-stone-curbed fireplace. The inner wall was made up of closely fitting stones, some of which had been removed from the floor area at the time it was dug and cleared. The space between the inner and outer wall was filled with earth making it into one continuous thick wall.

In the past animal skins might have covered the doorway but today it was open to the gale that lashed ineffectively outside. Inside all was calm and dry, with the candles providing enough light to see the construction details.

It was explained that when a good fire was lit there was no need for a chimney, the warm smoke simply drifted upwards to fill the top of the cone from where it percolated out through the thatch.

The timber framework caught my attention. About nine or ten, 3 metres high vertical posts, each as thick as a man's thigh, formed an inner circle about half way between the wall and the centre. The tops of these posts were connected together by a smooth and continuous circle of stout wooden lintels whose purpose was to support the considerable weight of the thatch that was pressing in all around. The shape was familiar, *'A continuous circle of stout uprights connected by a circle of lintels.'*

I pictured a fire lit in the central hearth with people living and dreaming their lives away within the shelter of a circle within a circle, and immediately connected it with another great circle within a circle. A question formed. *'If the design of this round house was typical of the larger Dartmoor round houses, could it begin to explain the evolution and design of Stonehenge or some of the larger stone circles?'* At once I felt nearer to understanding some of the ideas of these ancient people.

A second question followed. *If some of the larger round houses were used as meeting places for the local community, did this suggest that the shape of the circle itself had symbolic meaning relating to social gatherings. If so this adds further weight to the idea that the great stone circles were places of sanctuary where larger numbers of people assembled.*

On a sunny November day in 2004 I was delighted to be shown another recently constructed round house similar to the first. This is set in the Dartmoor grounds of Heatree House, surrounded by lap woven fences and items appropriate to life in the Neolithic or Bronze Age.

A Dartmoor round house.

Explanation: With the assistance of the Dartmoor National Park Authority, the Heatree Activity Centre have recreated a Bronze Age type of round house for educational purposes. It is set in a sympathetic environment and supported by activities representative of the time.

Inside a Round House
Explanation: This is from a simulation of a section of a prehistoric round house on display in Exeter Museum.

Left, explanation: Inside the Heatree round house. Note the inner circle of stout posts and lintels.

Food

Food used by the ancient dwellers was meat, grain, or fish from the streams, sometimes cooked by plunging hot stones into clay vessels dug into the floor, or perhaps grilled over the fire. Fuel was readily available from the plentiful trees that lined the valleys.

There is no reason to suppose that life for these early farmers was anything but good. It was certainly much more secure than the 'catch as catch can' of their hunter-gatherer ancestors.

Trade

Trade goods amply provide further proof of the civilised nature of the quality of their lives. Examples include the plentiful flint products that now litter, but are not native, to the moor and the stone or bronze axes and implements that may have originated from far away.

Trade requires traders, and traders need safe passage for their goods, together with security and comfort for themselves. This suggests that there were safe pathways across the moor, trade routes, accommodation, translators and guides, all the trappings of a civilised society.

Tin and Bronze

In the Bronze Age tin was in great demand not least as it formed the the alloy that, along with copper, was a consituent of bronze. This metal lay in plenty in the Dartmoor streams in a form that made it relatively easy to procure. Although at present there is no proof that tin was mined and traded by these early inhabitants, it seems likely.

Tools

The quality of a people's tools is another indication of their values, beliefs, and personalities. Fortunately there are enough tools surviving or copied to make some assessment.

Neolithic Axes

Prior to the Bronze Age crude but effective axes, scrapers and cutting tools were often chipped from flint nodules, these could have very sharp edges and some modern surgical instruments continue to make use of this technology.

Flint, together with a variety of tools from types of stone not native to Dartmoor, has been commonly found on the moor, suggesting that trade in such implements was not unusual.

Bronze Age Axes

Stone tools were probably in everyday use throughout the Bronze Age, perhaps used for everything from chopping meat and breaking bones to cutting down trees; but a variety of bronze axes began to appear.

The bronze axes shown here were made from copies of Bronze Age axe moulds. Moulds for casting bronze were found on Dartmoor. The finished product is an efficient use of bronze, providing a light and durable tool, capable of holding a sharp edge. Its design would have evolved from the stone axe to satisfy the need for a more efficient tool. If bronze axes were produced on Dartmoor it is sensible to suppose that the raw materials of tin and copper were also found locally.

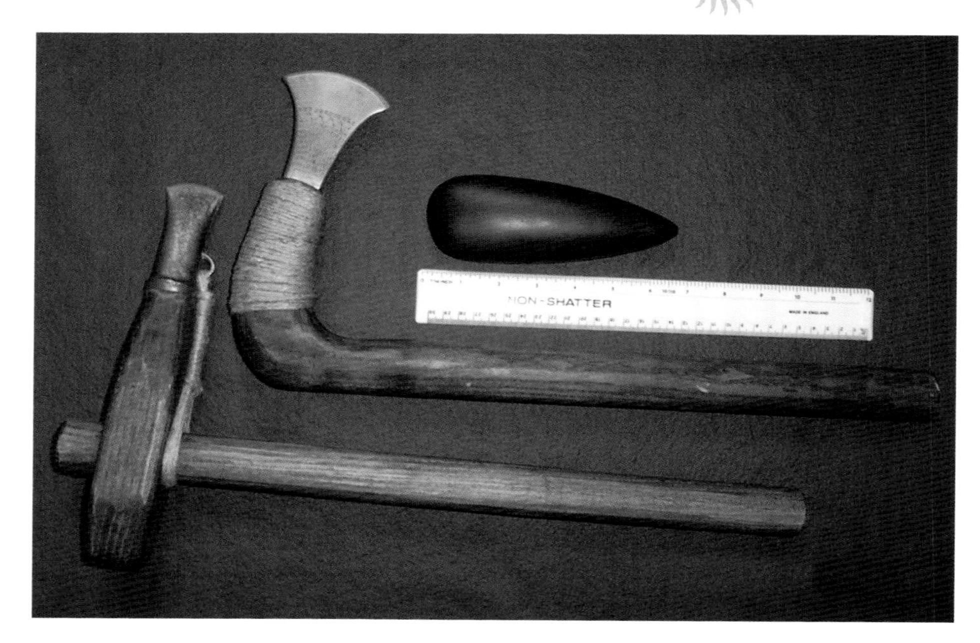

Bronze Age type axes from a collection by Martin Eddy of Caradon Countryside service, Cornwall

Two recently cast bronze axes, based on Dartmoor finds and a ceremonial quality stone axe.

The axe heads.

Courtesy of Martin Eddy of Caradon Countryside Service, Cornwall

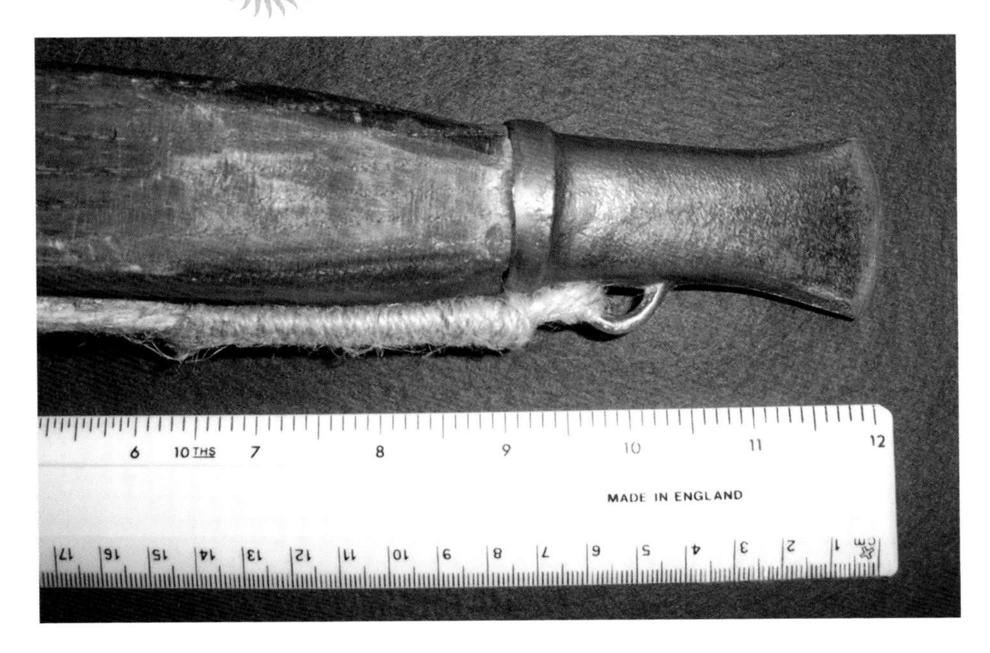

Tenon-headed axe.

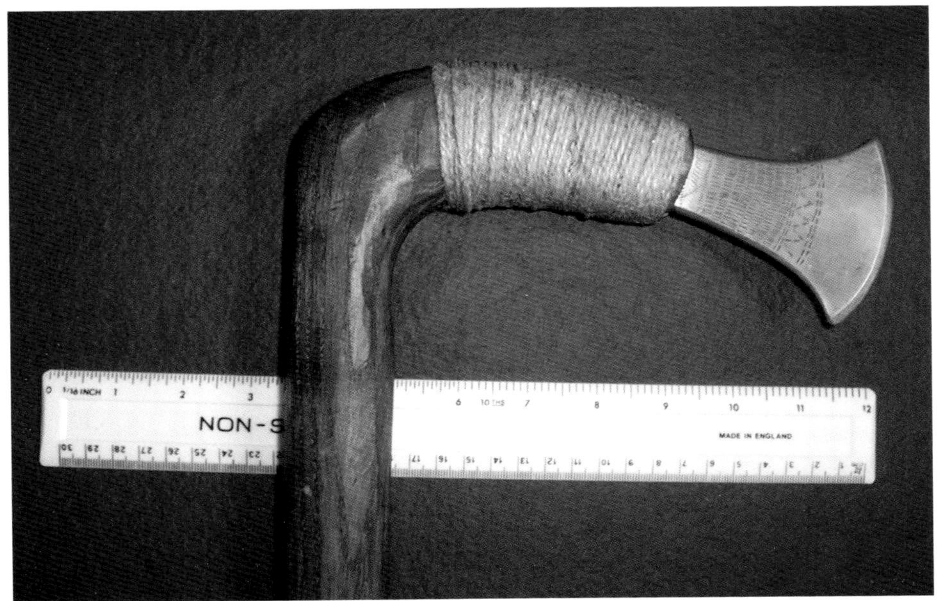

Simple bladed axe.

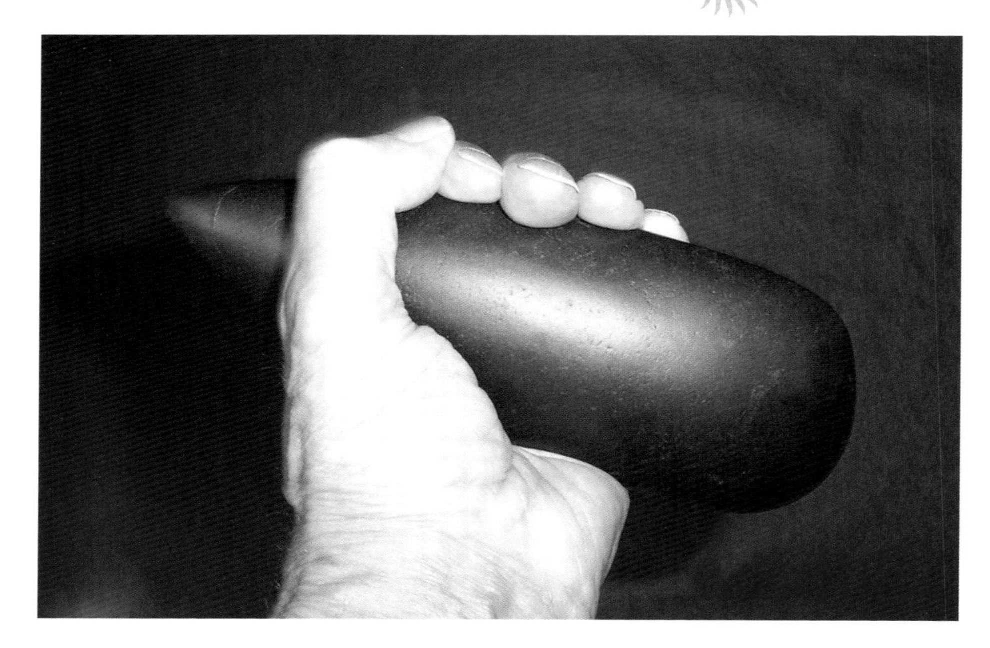

Hand axe side view.
Explanation: The origin of this axe is a mystery. It was discovered in a box of odds and ends at an auction. Its quality is beyond doubt for the smooth shape fits into the hand with all the balance of a tool evolved through centuries of use.

Hand axe, top edge.

Chapter Ten

Conclusions

Long ago the people of prehistoric Dartmoor left records of their lives and culture on the landscape. Some of this ancient chronicle continues to faithfully tell its story to all those who care to listen.

Part of the account was revealed one summer solstice evening at Hingston Hill's lonely monument high on Dartmoor. The setting sun aligned with the stone circle and a prominent cairn on a raised horizon; it was an obvious arrangement that called for further investigation.

At mornings around the time of the summer solstice, after sunrise, when the ground mists have dissipated and the sun ascends above any clouds near the horizon, many of the smaller stones cast their shadows to touch the next stone in the row.

Taking about an hour from sunrise to the time of the alignment, it begins with the shadow of the large standing stone at the head of the row projecting beyond the circle at sunrise. Then slowly the shadow shortens, tracking across the stone circle as the sun ascends. When the row is connected by its shadows, the pointed tip of the main megalith's shadow lays over the burial cist at the centre of the circle. As the sun rises higher the row's shadows shorten and move out of alignment.

This sophisticated and effective use of the solstice sun to link the occasion with the monument suggests its builders and their ancestors had a strongly developed spiritual sense and a good practical understanding of their environment.

Later investigations at Hingston Hill indicated how the site may have functioned as a calendar based on the positions of the setting sun throughout the year. This is a very carefully arranged construction, which avoids the problems of early morning mists and the artificially raised horizon, and provides a clear measure of sunset positions. The winter solstice sunset calibration with the tor is quite spectacular, and when corrections are made for the slight change in the sun's position since the monument's construction, its alignments are remarkably accurate.

These findings suggest that the placement of the positions of the main monuments on Hingston Hill is no longer an enigma:
The circle is positioned to align with the winter solstice sunset position and the tor.
The first megalith is placed to cast the tip of its shadow over the cist at the summer solstice.
The second megalith is placed to show the timing of the alignment.
The angle (azimuth) of the row is set to indicate the period two months (moonths) before and two months after the summer solstice.
The large cairn to the north-west of the circle aligns with the summer solstice sunset position.
The natural raised horizon to the west of the circle was improved by the erection of an ancient wall to provide an excellent measuring horizon for sunset positions as viewed from the circle throughout the year.

Possibly the most significant result of this investigation is the realisation that sun alignments with ancient monuments may be arranged to occur at any time of day or time of year. The implications of this are valuable for they provide another way to evaluate ancient monuments. For example the following tests may be made:

Does the monument come into alignment on a significant day?
Does the monument come into alignment at a particular time of day?
Does the monument align directly or by its shadows?

Although this exploration was concerned with the Dartmoor sun, once a sun calendar is located and understood, it may prove worthwhile to investigate it further for possible alignments with the moon or stars. However such alignments may be more difficult to prove.

The ingenuity of the design of Merrivale's double row layout and sun position indicators was revealed by:

1 Their combined east-to-west axis that points to the equinox sunset (and sunrise?), which is from the southern row's blocking stone in the east to the western end of the northern double row.

2 Their 'eastern end vector' (see diagram p.103) that points towards the summer solstice sunset position and the winter solstice sunrise position.

3 Their 'western end vector' (see diagram p.103) that points towards the summer solstice sunrise position and the winter solstice sunset position.

This investigation was limited to some of the more complex ancient Dartmoor sites on the assumption that there are probably routine functions for the types of monument that occur with greater frequently.

Examination of the technology used in these particular ancient Dartmoor monuments suggests they were part of a larger group that may have extended over Southern England, Western Europe and possibly the lands surrounding the Mediterranean.

Reliable calendars are necessary when people wish to expand and co-ordinate their practical and spiritual needs with those of their neighbours and their neighbour's, neighbours. There is a time to reap, a time to sow, a time to remember and a time to meet to celebrate and to pass on information, sometimes over a wide area. To achieve these objectives calendars must be synchronised so that agreed dates may be known and set up throughout the areas of co-operation. The Dartmoor sun provided this essential service through sun calendars, which were locally implemented in a variety of ways to suit particular sites.

The double rows at Merrivale were also found to provide an effective calendar based on the positions of the setting sun (rather than sunrise positions) for the same reasons as those at Hingston Hill.

Stonehenge and monuments on the European mainland were also investigated and found to employ similar calendar technologies to those used on Dartmoor.

It is interesting to realise that Merrivale's sophisticated double rows may have evolved from a more simple collection of monuments to the south of the double rows, in much the same way that Stonehenge is supposed to have developed from 3000BC to 1600BC. Perhaps this suggests a similar period of development for Merrivale.

The Dartmoor monuments observed suggested new ways to read some ancient sun calendars, and the Hingston Hill's monument indicated the advantage of a monument aligning after sunrise.

There were indications at Stonehenge that around 1600BC the summer solstice sunrise alignment may have occurred a minute or two after sunrise and that the existing Heel-stone was not intended to be on the monument's axis. A second Heel-stone, presently missing but with its socket clearly defined, would at the desired time have thrown its long shadow down the north side of the processional way. The existing Heel-stone's shadow would then have aligned with the south side, leaving the centre of the processional way lit by the early morning summer solstice sun.

Two of Drizzlecombe's stone rows indicate the importance their prehistoric builders gave to the winter solstice setting sun. The Merrivale and Hingston Hill monuments also emphasise this important time, when the old year dies and a new one is born.

Dartmoor's ancient monuments with their lack of defences and comfortable and permanent stone houses suggest the story of an epoch where land was plentiful and life was sweet, like childhood remembered. It is a story of wise travellers from far away lands; of wood, stone, the warm red of copper, the glow of bronze, and the gold of the Dartmoor Sun.

The Plymouth gnomon and circle.
Explanation: In the heart of the city of Plymouth, just a few miles from Hingston Hill's ancient row and circle, stands a modern monument constructed of shiny metal. A gnomon casts its shadow over a circle, telling the time of the day and the time of the year to those who know where and how to look.

References

Chapter 1

[1] Hemery Eric, *High Dartmoor*, Robert Hale – London 1983, pp. 158–9.

Chapter 5

[1] Krupp, Dr. E. C., *Echoes of the Ancient Skies*, Harper & Row 1983, p. 122.

[2] Butler, Jeremy. *Dartmoor Atlas of Antiquities, Volume Three – The South-West*, Devon Books 1994, *pp. 135 to 142*.

[3] Field Guide Number Eleven, *The Drizzlecombe Stone Rows,* by the Devon Archaeological Society, in association with Dartmoor National Park.

Chapter 6

[1] Butler, J., *Dartmoor Atlas of Antiquities, Volume Three – The South-West*, Devon Books 1994, p.25.

[2] SkyMap Pro.8 Software.

[3] Butler, J., *Dartmoor Atlas of Antiquities Volume Three – The South-West*, Devon Books 1994, p. 30.

[4] Christopher Knight & Robert Lomas, *Uriel's Machine*, Century 1999.

Chapter 7

[1] Carol Anderson, Philippe Planel & Peter Stone, *Stonehenge – A Teacher's Handbook,* English Heritage.

[2] SkyMap Pro.8 Software.

[3] *National Geographic*, January 2004, *Star Search*, by Harald Meller, Photographs by Kenneth Garrett, pp. 76–87.

[4] Christopher Knight & Robert Lomas, *Uriel's Machine,* Century 1999.

Chapter 8

[1] Wood, John Edwin, *Sun, Moon and Standing Stones*, Oxford University Press 1980, p. 134.

Chapter 9

[1] Dartmoor National Park Authority, *Merrivale an Archaeological Landscape*, English Heritage, 2004, p.19.